A Letter Away From

Asaba

Claudia Efemini

ISBN: 978-1-7393030-0-6

Also available as an eBook.

"A Letter Away From Asaba is a novella that speaks through history to resonate with us today. Claudia's writing is moving and deeply informed, shedding light on one of Nigeria's greatest tragedies. A stunning debut." – **Lily Laycock, editor of *A Letter Away From Asaba***

"Efemini's passion for history, her heritage, and shedding light on the Asaba massacre of 1967, is evident throughout the pages of *A Letter Away From Asaba.*" – **Hazel Peters, journalist, poet, and founder of No Permission Zine, a zine for Black and People of Colour in Scotland**

"Efemini's retelling of the Asaba massacre is an important read. Our stories need to be told through the wide lens that Nigerian history deserves." – **Chinny Ukata, co-author of *It's A Continent* (2022) and co-host of It's A Continent Podcast**

"In *A Letter Away From Asaba,* Efemini makes it known that history does not remain a thing of the past." – **Charlie Fjällman, avid reader**

"*A Letter Away From Asaba* is a suspenseful tale that seamlessly blends Nigerian history, Black British history, and European history. The epistolary novella style immerses readers in the characters, making them feel as though they are Onome and Chioma. The story delves into themes of identity, unity, and compassion, weaving together multiple perspectives and providing a captivating, unpredictable journey. It challenges readers by demonstrating that the line between good and bad is often blurred. The narrative is introspective and engages in a thoughtful critique of its own perspectives, subverting many preconceptions and offering insightful criticism of censorship. It underscores the importance of sharing everyone's story and is both enlightening and engaging. As readers learn, feel moved, and have their perspectives challenged while reading this remarkable novella, they will understand that it is not only a significant story about the past but also the future and the present, emphasising the importance of storytelling. Every British person, Nigerian, and African should read this." – **Ayobami Ruth Olufemi-White, co-founder of We Write and host of We Listen Podcast**

For the victims of the Asaba massacre, October 1967.

Dear reader,

2020 was the year that I submitted my International Baccalaureate Extended Essay on the British and Nigerian press censorship of the Asaba Massacre in October 1967. I still vividly recall the heavy sigh of relief that I let out when clicking the send button on outlook. Little did I know that the Asaba massacre would be so influential in my life. Little did I know that I'd weave the history of the Asaba massacre into a fictional narrative with the aim of educating people on the event.

Writing that essay was far from seamless. If you, like me, read the words 'Asaba massacre' for the first time and was perplexed yet intrigued, you would understand. The Asaba massacre remains neglected within the wider historiography of the Nigerian civil war. A sobering reality that I hope to change. My spontaneous decision to order Professors Elizabeth Bird and Fraser Ottanelli's book 'The Asaba Massacre: Trauma, Memory and the Nigerian Civil War' was unintentionally sapient. It was like opening the door to an array of hidden historical information about the event and how it was depicted within the press. Put simply, reading their research was influential in helping me write my extended essay and eventually writing this novella.

A year after the submission of this essay the thought of the Asaba massacre did not leave me. Even though I desperately tried to keep my mind focused on the present being my first-year university courses in international politics and early modern history, I couldn't help but drift back to my essay on the Asaba massacre. My thoughts would trail back to it every now and then. One monumental day, in early December 2021 as I was lying in bed in my student accommodation, I experienced a lightbulb moment that would eventually alter the trajectory of my life, paving the way for *A Letter Away From Asaba* to come into fruition. 'I should write a book about the Asaba massacre! A historical fiction to be precise.' was the thought wavering around my mind.

So, during the entirety of 2022 I devoted a large amount of my time to transforming my thoughts into reality through planning, writing, and editing this novella. The entire process was mostly enjoyable but there were some rollercoaster moments. I swiftly received a book deal from an independent publisher in London but as a young writer without a literary agent at the time I soon learnt that it was not the right place for me to publish my book. I made the brave decision to work towards self-publishing my work instead. Now, here I am writing the preface to my debut novel that I am set to self-publish. I am grateful for the journey and the range of individuals that I've encountered along the way as it has taught me plenty about book publishing and has greatly contributed to my personal growth.

I wrote this novella to enlighten people about the Asaba massacre and its press coverage as I was once enlightened back in 2020. Though it's historical fiction, I hope that readers take away the importance of the event and the cruciality of educating ourselves on microhistory, a term that I learnt in one of my lectures used to define the study of an event that provides conceptual understanding of wider themes in macrohistory. History is vital and relevant, contrary to what you might have been told or taught.

Claudia

Important note for all readers about the portrayal of characters:

A Letter Away From Asaba is a historical fictional epistolary novella. As such, some of the characters within this narrative are historical figures. However, it is important to note that both protagonists, Onome and Chioma, are fictional characters. Likewise, Kate, is an entirely fictional character and was by no means an actual historical individual during the time of the Asaba massacre. By stating this I hope to avoid potential misunderstandings about the portrayal of historical figures within this narrative.

<u>Part 1.</u>

1. Onome

9th October 1967

Dear Diary,

I'm still thinking about Nigeria.

I miss everything about it: the smell, the atmosphere, my family, and my dear friends. Especially my Chioma. I still remember the day that we met in primary school at the tender age of five. I had always been timid, especially as a child. I would often sit in the school compound digging holes with large sticks and filling them with sand and dust. Whilst the other children would play together, I was alone. But one special day, Chioma came and sat with me. Since then, we have remained best friends.

It has been a while since I last wrote to her. The last time I heard from her was right before the outbreak of civil war in our dear country Nigeria. Living in England, I commend the British for how effortlessly they have managed to legitimise the notion that 'barbaric' Africans are fighting each other on the grounds of internal division. All

9

without acknowledging how colonial rule in Nigeria has perpetuated this rife tribalism.

As an Urhobo girl from Bendel State, I have always grown up celebrating and praising Nigerian unity irrespective of the circumstances that trouble us. We are a people bursting with diversity, from the Edo, Urhobo, Isoko, Igbo, and more. Chioma is from Bendel State like myself but is tribally Igbo and we never fight due to our tribal differences. Instead, we constantly embrace our complexities.

Here in Britain, I've met quite a few Nigerians from different walks of life and tribal backgrounds. I've encountered Yorubas, Hausas, and Igbos and I do not feel any sort of tribal tension with them. But if we were to go back home, we would ideologically clash. Tunde's parents would be staunch supporters of the Action Group, whilst Chinua's parents would cast their vote for the National Council of Nigeria and the Cameroons. Or perhaps, as we are so few in Britain, we would feel obliged to stick together. That this idea of unity only presents itself when proven necessary.

I dream of Nigeria united. Every single day.

10th October 1967

Dear Diary,

I need to settle my thoughts about home and focus on London and my law degree. After all, my essay for contract law is due in a few days and it is certainly not going to write itself.

Every day I feel so privileged to be studying at such a prestigious university, but from time to time I tend to feel sorry for myself. This is simply because people do not understand what African and Caribbean students go through here in Britain. From the death stares on campus to having "Go back to your country" screamed at you on the street. Whenever I complain, my mother scorns me for being weak. As Britain is not my country, she believes I am obliged to accept the disrespect simply because I am getting a rich education. Very few Nigerians, not to talk of Nigerian women, get the opportunity to study in Britain. My mother describes me as a fish in an ocean full of seagulls: lucky, chosen. Though I fully understand the angle that she

11

is coming from, when will we Black people learn to stop accepting it?

The British do not understand.

Just this morning, I was walking through the busy streets of central London, surrounded by smart-dressed men on their way to work. Out of nowhere, I heard loud noises. No, it wasn't the churning of the birds or the honk of a horn pressed by an outraged driver. Neither was it the splatter of rain or the wheels of the big red buses on the rocky roads. It was the sound of voices screaming, resonating in my chest.

As I took a left towards Drury Lane, I noticed a group of people approaching the university campus. They resembled a wave of fire, full of energy as they screamed out the top of their lungs. The closer they got to me, the larger and louder the group appeared to be.

They were chanting two phrases - "Stop sending arms!" and "Free Biafra!". I soon realised that it was a protest against Britain's decision to send arms in support of the Nigerian army against

Biafran forces. As the protestors marched past me, I noticed a woman in all-black clothes and black boots. She had long braids with brown beads at the end. I couldn't help but smile at the sight of an African woman refusing to conform in the white man's land. My untidy self-braided jumbo braids couldn't compete with her neat, sophisticated hairstyle.

What drew my attention to this woman was the banner she held up. It read "Asaba", more accurately "Free Asaba". Asaba, the very town that my dearest friend Chioma is from. Without thinking, I immediately darted towards her, pushing past the bulk of people marching down that street. I asked her what was going on and her face dropped. Before she continued marching, I specifically asked her about the meaning of her banner. She turned to face me, and her face dropped again, spiralling into deep sadness.

She told me that people in Asaba were being massacred and that her friend had been killed. The rhythm at which her strong, sharp pidgin bounced off her tongue agitated my worry. Before

13

she could explain more, hysterical crying broke out amongst the crowd.

2. Chioma

3rd October 1967

My dearest Onome,

How you dey? The past few days have been hectic to say the least. As you are probably aware, civil war has broken out. Though I sort of expected it, I always had a tiny part of me that hoped for a compromise between the separatists and the pro-unity people. But the bitter truth is that negotiation is hardly ever possible in a troubled country like this.

When will Nigeria ever celebrate unity? Take you and me for example. We are both inhabitants of Bendel State and yet come from differing tribes. Our differences shape who we are, and our friendship does not consist of pitting those differences against each other but rather embracing these very differences. Though I understand the Biafrans' hope for secession, as an Igbo person I think Nigeria is a lot stronger when unified.

Separation will only result in hostility and confusion. I say we keep things the way they are.

For this very reason, I will be attending the welcome ceremony on the streets of Asaba this Friday, 6th October. I am so excited to witness the Nigerian troops walk through Asaba. For keeping us unified, they deserve to be celebrated. They are doing our country an incredible favour, trust me. My great aunt, Amaka, even has the honour of presenting a traditional woven cloth to the commander as part of the Omu of Asaba. Though she is currently fighting pneumonia so I doubt she will attend; hopefully her condition improves in the coming days. I was so insanely adamant about contributing in some way, so the organiser of the ceremony agreed that I help design the banners. They will read "One Nigeria", two words that I am so incredibly passionate about as you already know. I shall paint it green and white to represent the colours of our dear flag. Anyways, how are things back in Lon...

12th October 1967

Dear Diary,

My hands are shaking and I'm trembling, but I must write. There's no other option.

Chukwuemeka and I attended the welcome ceremony. I barely finished my banners before Chukwuemeka dragged me out of the house. As we approached the large crowd on the street, I felt an incredible sense of joy. As embarrassed as I am to admit it, it felt so special waiting for Nigerian soldiers to march through the street just across from my house. I felt so lucky to witness the greatness of the very men striving to unify the nation. I felt sorry for Aunty Amaka who couldn't be there, still recovering from pneumonia. I felt sorry for Onome, who's all the way in London. I thought back to how shattered we were when General Ojukwu announced the secession of Biafra. I questioned whether dividing Nigeria would cause us to suffer a similar fate to Germany. The Eastern and Western split has seen one side embracing democracy and developing into a prosperous economy, and the other practising communism and perishing.

At the welcome ceremony, I saw people I had never seen before. People who had travelled from their remote villages were to be present at the event. Everyone was dressed extravagantly in our traditional white attire – *akwa ocha*, symbolising peace. As I looked around, I saw plentiful faces filled with pure joy. Chukwuemeka was expectedly dressed in his Nigerian football jersey that he bought when we were in Lagos earlier this year. I had never seen him beam so widely dressed in the colours of our dear flag.

A screech sounded from a distance as the soldiers began their approach. They looked so determined and strong with their uniform and heavy weaponry. They marched collectively, a march that reminded me of a disciplined orchestra, violinists changing the direction of their bow in synchronisation. Many of the soldiers had glowing dark skin and slender bodies, resembling true Hausa men. The closer they got to us, the more I began to feel a sense of utter confusion. Their expressions perplexed me. I understood that army men were not supposed to smile but their faces mirrored plain disgust. At first, I thought it was the smell of the street because the streets of Asaba are certainly not pleasant. But the men resembled red and anger. I thought that maybe they had not been expecting a large crowd as the welcome ceremony had been kept a secret to surprise the soldiers.

Before I could even utter a welcome, the soldiers started charging toward us. People scattered like flies whilst others began to panic and barely moved. My legs trembled and I saw a soldier grab a rifle gun from his right-hand side and point it towards a young man attempting to de-escalate the situation. This is when I registered that this was in fact real life. That the federal troops had chosen to attack despite our blatant ambivalence and respect. The soldiers began to detain any man that they could get their hands on. Several women who witnessed their husbands and sons being mishandled began to get on their knees and pray. I could not believe my eyes. The soldiers were violently harassing the people of Asaba. The very people that were standing and holding up banners to welcome them and thank them for their service.

The shock caused me to lose track of my breathing. Oh, what a fool I was to believe that I was regarded as a Nigerian and not a Biafran! As I looked to Chukwuemeka, soldiers grabbed him viciously by the arm and escorted him to a smaller crowd of captured men. I lunged over to free my brother but I suddenly felt a hand over my mouth, a stranger pulling me behind the bush. When I faced the man, I saw he was not a soldier. Tall and dressed in ordinary clothes, he assured me that he wasn't dangerous and that he saw the disruption in the area and wanted to help someone, and I had been closest to him. His name was Femi.

I was too frightened to question him, even as he led me away. I tried to look back for Chukwuemeka. But all I could see were hundreds of women on their knees. Chukwuemeka was gone.

As we walked, I kept querying where we were going, and Femi kept ignoring me. I wondered how he could walk seemingly free of fear, whilst I could barely move. All I could think about was the ferocity of the soldiers. When the sounds of panic

20

faded, he finally turned to me. Said we were going to stay with his friend. I demanded to know who, refusing to be treated like an animal led on a leash.

He told me his friend's name was David, and that he had connections with the diaspora in Britain and America. That I could send letters through him if I wished.

3. Onome

17th November 1967

Dear Chioma,

It has been a while since we last wrote to each other. You did not finish the last sentence in the letter you sent me. Hopefully, you are not in any kind of trouble. I have been hearing troubling things about Asaba.

I am very well, though studying law is certainly testing my academic capabilities. To be frank, though, my degree is the least of my concerns. Yes, I have heard about the civil war in Nigeria. As much as you are shocked that it has come to this, the longer I live in London the more I realise that it was somewhat inevitable. You see, this was carefully planned by the British from the moment they stepped foot in Nigeria and united a bunch of tribes under one rule. Their propaganda cannot fool me. Can you believe that they are portraying the war as something that only involves Nigerians and are not claiming any responsibility at all? How foolish!

But I must tell you about what I saw on my way to university. A protest. An organised protest against Britain's decision to send arms to the federal government in support of Nigerian troops against Biafrans. I know that we are generally supportive of the unity cause, but as I am seeing events unfold here in London, I think we might be mistaken. We must ask ourselves why the British are so persistent in supporting Nigerian unity. Maybe the Biafrans do have a point. Someone that is deemed a threat to the oppressor might have a valid point in the grand scheme of things. How do we even know that Nigerian unity is what is best for us? That is the rubbish that the British and our fellow people from Bendel State have been feeding us. We must remember that Nigeria was not Nigeria until the British claimed that it was. We need to acknowledge that Bendel State is so tribally diverse so it might be hard for us to grasp the flaws of a united Nigeria. Especially as an Igbo person, do you not ever sympathise with some of the Biafrans' views at all?

At the protest, a woman was holding a banner that read "Free Asaba". When I asked, this woman told me about a massacre that had happened there and that one of her friends had fallen victim. Is this true at all? I pray that she received false information because it just sounds so unusual and unlikely. Massacred by who? Armed robbers? Biafran soldiers? Terrorists? British colonial masters? Or even our very own Nigerian soldiers? She did not specify so I have been trying to make sense of what she told me. I do not doubt a word that this woman told me because she was bursting with emotions. Unless she is a commendable actress, I am concerned for Asaba. I do hope you and Chukwuemeka are safe and well.

The British press has not covered anything on Asaba at all. So please, all I beg of you is to inform me of what has happened. Nothing else. I am praying for the people of Asaba from my little student room in London. Get back to me as soon as you possibly can.

Onome

25th November 1967

Dear Diary,

Today has been an eventful day. It started with me clumsily spilling my cup of tea all over the office table. At that moment, I was convinced that my internship at *The Daily Times* was drifting away before my eyes. But to my surprise, my support officer was not bothered at all. He understood how nervous I was on my first day and reassured me that I was there to learn and not outperform my experienced colleagues. As comforting as that sounded, the bitter truth is that I had to be nervous. People like me are required to work ten times harder to get the opportunities that our English counterparts get. Securing this internship was a whole journey. From initially rejecting me because they claimed they had already accepted "enough Black students" as part of their racial quota scheme, to frowning at my African surname and consequently asking for more sample essays than my English friend Kate, who applied for the same internship.

My support officer is a man named Peter. A prudent and inquisitive Englishman in his sixties with a deep interest in writing and telling peoples' stories. Upon hearing that I was from Nigeria, as expected, he began to ramble on about the civil war. I was pleasantly surprised at how much he knew. Dare I say it, he knows more about where I come from than I do. I blame the colonial education system in Nigeria; I could delve into Britain during the First World War, or give you facts about the Tudors, but I could barely tell you anything about Nigeria during pre-colonial times.

Before I started this internship at *The Daily Times,* I had told Kate about my plans to write about the Nigerian Civil War. Her response was pure laughter. Not because she didn't think I was capable but because she felt my words would counter their agenda. According to Kate, my work will likely remain unpublished so long as it is misaligned with the newspaper's agenda. I couldn't understand her view, I always thought that *The Daily Times* was a more liberal newspaper. I would've understood if I was working at *The Daily Sketch* because of their conservative, degrading views on African affairs. So, I desperately hoped that she was mistaken.

But I was the one proven mistaken. Whilst Peter was well educated on Nigeria as a country, as soon as I started to contribute to the conversation, I noticed a sense of irritation in him. It was not only evident facially but displayed in his entire body. It was almost as if he could not bear to hear the view of a Nigerian. Ironically, the topic of conversation was centred around my country of birth, not his. I urged him to ask his manager if I could get the opportunity to write a weekly column on Nigeria, given the growing concern of the Nigerian diaspora in Britain. I thought I had convinced him enough because he seemed to be fond of the idea, but the moment I mentioned interviewing people in Nigeria to uncover the 'real story', he grew cold. He assured me that that would not be necessary and that there was already an experienced team working on the developing situation in Nigeria. At that point, I knew I couldn't even mention Asaba. The fact that he knew about an entire civil war in Nigeria and was not willing to hear from the people on the ground

27

meant that he would certainly not give voice to the people of tiny, little Asaba.

After work, I bustled my way through autumn leaves to get to Kate's flat, itching to tell her all about my first day. When I arrived, Kate took a while to open the front door. She welcomed me in her dressing gown; she had been sleeping like an owl after submitting her essay for contract law. I didn't blame her. Studying law was unbearable at times. From endless reading lists to the thick, heavy books we had to carry to each lecture.

We sat down and Kate excitedly pressed me about my first day. I tried my best to appear as exhilarated as her but at the back of my mind, I remembered Peter and his hostility surrounding Nigeria. I told her that I had learnt a lot about the press industry, at least. But she eventually eked out the truth. I told her that she had been right. Right about the fact that I couldn't write about Nigeria, that the idea of conducting interviews disturbed Peter. Feeling smug, Kate asked me what exactly I was interested in covering in Nigeria. Immediately I began to ramble on about the unspoken massacre in Asaba and the woman at the protest holding a 'Free

28

Asaba' banner. I told her that I was still waiting for Chioma to send me a letter.

Kate seemed sceptical about the whole Asaba situation. I am so sure that she thinks I'm just making it all up. I wish she was there to witness the protest and the conversation I had with that woman that day. Though I often speak to Kate about affairs in Nigeria, she always seems to embody a simultaneous look of disinterest and intrigue. It is as though she wants to know my opinions on everything but never has anything tangible to add to the conversation. Although this time, she had something to say. She told me that she had been reading the newspaper and Asaba had been mentioned in the *Daily Times*. Kate read that Asaba is calm and all is well, with many civilians returning to their homes after some small disturbances. She reassured me not to worry and I felt immense relief. Surely, this means Chioma is safe.

29

4. Chioma

1st January 1968

Dear Onome,

I honestly cannot even believe that I am writing to you right now. It is all thanks to my new friends, Femi and David. I will tell you all about them but first, I must tell you about what is going on here in Asaba. I attended the welcome ceremony and it was horrible. After all my hard work in preparing several banners and dressing up in white, the behaviour of the Nigerian soldiers only proved my deep naivety.

When the soldiers approached the large crowd they began to harass us and violently captured all the men, even Chukwuemeka, right before my eyes. I don't know what they did to them, perhaps they enlisted them all into the army, or worse still, killed them. I try not to ponder around the different possibilities as it's so upsetting. I've not heard from Chukwuemeka at all. Femi has assured me that he is fine and that he will get in contact with me as soon as he can. But I believe Femi is only telling me this to alleviate my anxiety. Chukwuemeka does not even know Femi, nor does he know where I am right now. I cannot return to my home as it is a danger zone and word of the area is that the soldiers have looted all our goods.

I cannot even attempt to explain to you how awful the soldiers have been. They even had the audacity to gather all the women up and only God knows what they subjected them to. I was so lucky because Femi happened to be walking by and saw the disturbances at the welcome ceremony. He dragged me out of the situation and we managed to escape. I am currently staying at his friend David's house. It's safe for now but we aren't sure for how long. David's connections to the diaspora is the only thing giving me strength in my despair. It's thanks to him that I'm able to keep in contact with you. He doesn't want to reveal to me how he has been able to send the letters. I just sincerely hope that we do not get caught. If the Nigerian troops were to read the contents of our letters, I would almost certainly be killed. Hardly anyone in Nigeria, let alone abroad, is aware of what

31

happened in Asaba just some months ago. It has become taboo to even speak about it. That is why I was so happy to hear that you saw that woman with the "Free Asaba" banner. It must've been fate that you saw her! Onome, I need you to find out her whereabouts and everything she knows. She might even know more than I do because I was saved before anything further happened. I cannot believe that they would kill her friend like that. It only worries me even more thinking about Chukwuemeka and all the other people I saw that day.

I am so frustrated and confused. You personally know how patriotic I am, or rather was. I never for a second thought to see Nigeria from the perspective of the Biafrans even though I'm Igbo. To be honest, I think that people in Asaba were targeted due to our tribe. After all, the enemy of the Nigerian soldiers is the Igbo man.

I hope you are okay and progressing well in your studies. I beg of you to find that woman and ask her more questions. For the sake of Chukwuemeka, I, and everyone here in Asaba. Our story must be told, and the Nigerian soldiers must be held accountable. Also, please pray for us all. I

32

cannot tell you exactly how long we will last here at David's until the soldiers come for us too.

Chioma

P.S.

I apologise for the abrupt ending to my previous letter. I was just so ecstatic about the welcome ceremony that I forgot to finish writing.

12th January 1968

Dear Diary,

I feel so worthless still staying here.

I miss my home. Though I'm enjoying getting to know both David and Femi, it is not the same as being in the comfort of family. Here, I am confined to playing a character. I can no longer sing along to my favourite jazz tunes or paint pictures as I did in my own home. If I bring out too much of my bubbly self, I irritate them. I'm worried I'll end up homeless. I wish I could just go home, but it is too risky in this current climate of war. I am scared to go outside alone because all I can think about is the federal soldiers. The trust that I once had for the very men that were supposed to fight to protect our nation has dispersed like dust.

This morning there was a knock at the door. I could see how scared David and Femi were even though they tried to conceal it. David got up to answer the door and ordered Femi and me to go upstairs and hide underneath the bed in case it was a soldier planning to loot. Rumours had been going around that the soldiers have been looting homes and, in the process, raping women. I hate to think that's probably why those women were all gathered in a herd when I took my final glance back at the welcome ceremony.

As we lay flat side-by-side underneath David's bed, I turned to face Femi. He looked back at me, pupils dilated, and reached out to hold my hand. I flinched with fear and removed my hand far away from his reach. I had no interest in either of the men I lived with and wanted that to be clear. To steer away from the awkward situation, I quietly thanked Femi for saving me that day. I had not properly thanked him for his courageous decision to spare my life at the welcome ceremony. Femi let out a warm smile. Without Femi, my fate would have been in the hands of the federal troops, and I would've almost certainly ended up amongst those women left vulnerable.

David soon came back upstairs to tell us we were clear to come out. According to him, it was a neighbour who was telling him about the rife looting by soldiers in Asaba after the massacre. Ironically, Femi had suggested that that would happen the day I met him. He had accurately predicted that after the soldiers had dealt with the people, they would start going into people's houses to threaten and rob them of their goods. He was completely right. Thankfully both of my parents are currently residing in Lagos so nobody would be at home.

Later.

Still, at the back of my mind, I can't help but wonder. How did Femi know what would happen? And why, out of everyone there that day, did he save *me*?

5. Onome

14th February 1968

Dear Chioma,

I'm at a loss for words. I would ask how you are, but I think your letter says it all. Asking that question would neither help your situation nor be of any significance.

Firstly, I'm so sorry about what happened at the welcome ceremony. I was so excited for you. Upon hearing about the massacre, I should have put two and two together and realised that the welcome ceremony was the event that resulted in a massacre. What happened to Chukwuemeka, and all those men and women is unacceptable and as Femi has said, I too want to extend my strong belief in Chukwuemeka still being alive. He will get in contact with you when he can, I highly hope that they have not done him any harm. It is quite possible that they enlisted him into the army without his consent, unfortunately. But let's be hopeful that that is not the case.

37

As for the rumours surrounding looting, my friend Kate told me about an article she read in the Daily Times on the situation in Asaba. Though there were some disturbances (which is probably what you experienced at the welcome ceremony), people have been returning to their homes. It might be safe for you to go back now, after all, Asaba is the least of Nigeria's problems. Who knows, maybe the people spreading these rumours are exaggerating. You know how us Nigerians tend to use hyperbole in any situation that proves fitting. We are a people bursting with emotion!

Those soldiers should be deeply ashamed of their actions. For them to just assume that you were all against them because of your Igbo ethnicity is diabolical.

It feels selfish for me to start telling you about my own personal concerns given the disastrous state that you must be in, but I hope I can provide some distraction. I started my internship at the Daily Times this week. I was discussing the civil war with my support officer, and he was so dismissive of my thoughts and ideas surrounding the war. I was going to mention Asaba but thought it would be pointless. If I'm able to pick up the courage to ask him about doing a case study on Asaba then I will. But the outlook is grim.

It's strange how Asaba's description in the English newspapers juxtaposes your experience. There are two possibilities - either the British are hiding the reality of what is going on or people in Asaba are exaggerating the situation. I must find the woman from the protest and speak to her to find out more. It will be a tough mission, but I will do my very best to try and locate her whereabouts and get all the information that I can. Please stay safe!

Onome

19th February 1968

Dear Diary,

I deeply regret sending that letter to Chioma. But now it has already been sent so there is nothing that I can do to stop it. I am like a photographer that has seen a beautiful bird and reached for their camera only for it to fly away. Except whilst the photographer has no control over the bird's motion, I made the disgraceful choice to send the letter even after reading it over and over. I have a deep feeling that I have come across as slightly insensitive. My only hope is that Chioma does not take it the wrong way. I doubt she will. Chioma is someone that tends to hide her emotions to appear strong and absolutely despises self-pity. I felt it was best to convince her that there is little to no danger in Asaba. After all, the article that Kate read and told me about practically confirms my instinct that the events of Asaba are being largely overemphasised. I do not doubt what Chioma has told me, but I do know that Asaba is not heavily involved in the conflict. The idea of soldiers looting innocent people's homes seems erratic to me. Had it occurred in Nsukka or Enugu my response might have been different.

I thought that if I could read the article Kate mentioned, I could lay these feelings to rest. Then, I could assure Chioma myself. I called Kate and asked if we could meet in the evening. I didn't tell her about my sudden interest in the newspaper article that she vaguely mentioned, thinking that I didn't want to overly involve her. It wasn't her struggle. I already regretted telling Chioma that I don't wholly believe her view of the Asaba massacre, it would be foolish of me to project the same disbelief on Kate too. Then I would be planting two seeds for trouble.

When I got to Kate's flat, we spoke about what we usually do, university and family. I found the perfect way to bring up the newspaper. I told her about the recent opening of the Winter Olympics in France which I truly have no interest in. Cleverly, I asked her for a newspaper so I could read more updates on the events. Kate was rather startled by my request. But she didn't raise too much of an eyebrow and began to scramble through books on her large shelf for a newspaper. I watched her like a rat waiting for a human to leave the kitchen so it can devour crumbs left on the kitchen counter.

Finally, Kate handed me a newspaper that she found under a pile of heavy history books, and I began to search. Instead of looking for an article covering the Olympics, my eyes scanned the pages in search of the word "Asaba". To my misfortune, I didn't find a single paragraph on the Nigerian Civil War, let alone Asaba. I flicked back to the front page only to realise that it was the *London Evening Standard.* Kate had told me the article was in the *Daily Times*. I tried my best to hide my frustration. So much frustration that I even asked her why there was no information on the Nigerian Civil War in the whole newspaper. But I doubt she was phased by this because she simply shrugged and said that she'd thrown the newspaper in the bin yesterday on her way to campus because she didn't need it anymore. My heart dropped. The one piece of evidence that could've convinced Chioma that her paranoia was spiralling was no longer within my reach. Or so I thought.

I left Kate's flat early, complaining about a sudden headache. Truthfully, my head was completely fine. I was simply infuriated that she had thrown it away. I still believe there was a motive behind it. Kate is a hoarder who takes comfort in keeping items that she doesn't need anymore. A torn anti-communist pamphlet from 1955 on top of her microwave testifies to that. So why would she just throw it away knowing its importance to me? Kate's nonchalant behaviour concerning Nigeria is unacceptable. If she wants to be friends with a Nigerian, she must sympathise with one too. Not so long ago, her ancestors were colonial masters in Nigeria!

Quite serendipitously, I passed a large, black communal bin at the corner of the road. A thought occurred to me and I ran over to the bin, opened it and began to search. Luckily the bin was on a quiet street, and I quickly spotted a *Daily Times* newspaper poking out near the top.

The newspaper is right beside me as I'm writing this. Though it's tattered and smells of rotten bananas, it's complete without a sign of a tear.

6. Chioma

29th March 1968

Dear Onome,

I have been tossing and turning all night contemplating whether I should even bother writing this letter to you. But God convinced me that I should, and it is for that reason only that I am reaching out to you for possibly the last time. No, it's not because it's so dangerous here in Asaba that I fear for my life. Rather, it is your belittlement of my struggles.

Britain has changed you. I don't know why this is the first time that I'm noticing it but I'm so thankful that I have finally been able to see it. Do you remember when we were younger, and we used to gossip about how our older cousins would change after going to study abroad? Their accents would suddenly sound more English, and their body language would be transformed to the point that even the way they walked was completely different on their return to Nigeria. But Onome, your change

44

is deeper than all of that. It is one that cuts deep into one's soul and leaves them scarred forever. How dare you! Did you even think to read through your letter before carelessly sending it off? Even I who is confined to writing letters in a hurried, secret fashion can refrain from such thoughtless ignorance. I hate to say it, but you are slowly becoming one of them. A descendant of colonists who belittle our continent and undermine our experiences to dodge responsibility for their despicable actions.

It's so disturbing how indoctrinated you have become since studying at King's College in London. Though it would've been lovely to have the opportunity to study abroad, now that I read your thoughts, I'm so glad that I haven't. Perhaps I would've been just as ideologically flawed as you. But it's not your fault. Rather the fault of your surroundings. That Kate friend of yours seems to be bad news. Who cares if she told you about a Daily Times newspaper article that rationalised the destruction in Asaba as solely "some disturbances" and claims that people are returning to their homes? Does that then suddenly prove reliable and

45

justify you to be so dismissive of the massacre that happened in my hometown?

The irony is that whilst you tell me that your Support Officer was so dismissive of your ideas during your first day at your internship at that very foolish Daily Times, you, too, are replicating his actions and channelling them to me. Do you not reckon that you are also seeking to undermine the very events that I am risking my, Femi, and most importantly David's life to tell you? Every time I send you a letter revealing the actions of the Nigerian soldiers, I risk our lives. I haven't even told Femi and David that I'm telling you all the intrinsic details of the massacre. If I do, they will stop me at once. If we get caught disclosing information, the soldiers will probably kill or lock us up for the rest of our lives. Just look at what happened to Wole Soyinka, who engaged in secretive meetings to avoid civil war. He is now suffering in jail simply because his actions did not conform to that of the Nigerian government. Even people in Lagos are unaware of the Asaba massacre but you, a Nigerian student all the way in London have been informed because I felt it was necessary and that you deserved to know. I didn't even ask you to make noise about it and spread the news because I thought you cared enough for me to do it regardless.

The most pathetic aspect of your letter is how you describe the personality of the Nigerian. You claim that we are "a people bursting with emotions" and for that reason, we are "exaggerating". Please, I beg you to eradicate that flawed mindset as it does more harm than good. You more than anyone should be aware of how Nigerians are a people of radical conformity. One suffers, we all suffer. One celebrates, we all celebrate. One fight, we all fight. It's the people of Europe and America who tend to exaggerate small situations. If the Asaba massacre had occurred in New York or London, I'm almost certain that the whole world would be aware of it. My dear sister, you are severely lost. Nigerians get on with things and make little to no noise about such instances. But in Britain, any small thing that happens causes a huge stir within society.

If you are too blind to see the bigger picture - in simple terms that the British are covering up the truth, I request that you stop contacting me for a while. At least until I get back to my normal life. Unfortunately for you, a lot of the substance of my letters will be composed of the Asaba massacre because I'm currently experiencing the aftermath. It isn't just an event that can be swiftly forgotten. I don't think that you realise the vast amount of people in Asaba that have lost cousins, fathers, sons, and mothers. This is not a scene from an action book, it's very much reality for me. So, if you cannot sympathise with that then it's best for us to go our separate ways, at least for the time being.

Chioma

7th April 1968

Dear Diary,

I woke up in the middle of the night yesterday. Thoughts muddled my mind. Everything from Chukwuemeka, the mystery of Femi, the Asaba massacre and Onome. Oh, Onome. Her insensitive words stick to me.

I thought too about my brother and the pressing need for me to find him. The day before, I had taken an unsuccessful trip around the neighbourhood asking if anyone had seen a tall, slim, fair-skinned boy with a Nigerian football jersey on. But every single person that I asked had no inclination of where he was. I hope and pray that Chukwuemeka is safe, possibly with Aunty Amaka. I have been heavily contemplating going to Aunty Amaka's house, but Femi has warned me that it still is not yet fully safe to roam the streets freely. That people looking for Biafran sympathisers could be anywhere. Even though I have not heard news of soldiers still being in Asaba, I still fear that Femi might be right.

49

But Femi's integrity remains unknown. He was so sure that soldiers were looting homes before anyone else knew. I fear he might be a spy of a larger force. Naivety has become a common theme in my recent life. I and plenty of the people in Asaba were tricked into organising and executing a welcome ceremony for the soldiers only for us to be brutally oppressed. I have to start expecting the worst of people. For me, it seems unlikely that Femi would spare a stranger's life whilst risking his own, asking for nothing in return.

This morning, I heard David and Femi downstairs discussing the civil war. The soldiers might have temporarily gone, but the massacre still haunts this town. Many of us have changed position from ambivalence to pro-Biafra and there are some radicals that yearn for revenge. I would not be surprised if some try to get in touch with the Biafrans to pressurise the French into supplying arms for a planned attack against the Nigerian army. But I do not hope for such actions. All I want is for our stories to be told, whether it be through press coverage or art. If only I was in London with the knowledge that I currently possess. I would have more freedom to bring this story to light.

Surprisingly when I got downstairs, Femi wanted to speak to me. We had rarely shared anything about our private lives so I played along, hoping to uncover more about his true intentions. He told me that the least we can do to ease the uncomfortable situation in Asaba is to genuinely get to know each other. So, I told him that I was 19 years old, from Asaba, and hoping to study at university next year. Cunningly, I threw the question back at him, itching to know who he really was. He paused for a while before answering. Femi is significantly older than me, I presume about thirty years old. He's from Lagos but is currently living in Asaba as he works in the oil industry. Not a surprise at all, the Delta region is incredibly rich in oil reserves. He works in Warri. I remember how my eyes widened at the word 'Warri' because that is where Onome is from.

There had been a question that I was burning inside to ask Femi. The question of why he chose to specifically save me from the massacre. I couldn't comprehend why he saved me as opposed

51

to an elderly woman less likely to fend for herself. Eventually, I managed to speak up and ask for the truth.

My preconceptions proved to be quite accurate. Femi is a Nigerian soldier, or rather was. He told me everything. He claims it was a spontaneous decision to save me. But what was interesting was his reasoning for doing it. As a soldier, he learned that your life could go one of two ways. You could use your power to mobilise the people in pursuit of good intentions. Or, you could allow your personality to be slowly poisoned, leading to inevitable corruption. Certain acts of evil and brutality that were once regarded to be foul have become more acceptable and desirable amongst the soldiers of today. You become numb and insensitive to torture and suffering. Femi believes that this misuse of power is what enabled the army to behave the way they did.

I now understand his composure on our way to David's house that day. Surely as a former army man, he has witnessed such acts, or even worse, attacked innocent civilians in the past? Apathy is a sorry aftereffect of too much bloodshed. I don't know where he served and whether he was forcefully enlisted. If he wishes to share that information with me later, so be it, but I will not force it out of him. I think he can be trusted now. Or at least, I sincerely hope so.

7. Onome

14th May 1968

Dear Chioma,

I know that you told me to not contact you but that is impossible for me. Every day that goes by I think about you. I wonder how you are doing and about the current state of Asaba. All I can do is sincerely apologise for the heartless, ignorant letter that I sent to you. There is no way that I can justify my actions. Asaba was the last place that I would've expected such havoc to occur. For that reason, I was searching for ways to convince myself that the situation was not as torturous as it was. That was so very wrong of me. As for the newspaper that Kate told me about, I have it with me and have looked through it thoroughly. Before you get outraged, I promise you that I do not believe anything that the Daily Times claims. But my law degree has taught me to acknowledge opposing views to further strengthen your argument. Therefore, it would be smart for me to gather as much evidence of the

British press providing false narratives of the Asaba massacre in order to make sufficient claims against it.

The words 'Britain has changed you' triggered an epiphany in me. You're completely right. The fact that I even considered it to be true is disgraceful. The fact that I accused Nigerians of exaggerating the disturbances instead of trying to understand the situation fully is exactly something that my support officer would applaud me for. But instead, it isn't a middle-aged, wealthy, English man doing it. It's me. I am supposed to be your best friend, a Nigerian who doesn't look down on fellow Nigerians but here I am doing exactly what I claim to despise.

One thing that I can assure you of is that I can finally see Kate's condescending nature in clear view. This was even before I received your letter, so we are on the same page with regard to her behaviour. She doesn't have an ounce of empathy when it comes to the effect of colonialism on Nigeria. She is a symptom of the bigger problem. I cannot stop thinking about how the Nigerian and British governments have removed the massacre

55

from public memory. But they don't know that our friendship exists and that the letters that we constantly send each other have unfolded the process of something immaculate. We, as a unit, are going to bring forward the story of the Asaba massacre. It's the right thing to do.

You experienced it first-hand, so we have a primary witness. As you're still in Asaba, you can find people to interview. On my end, I can counter the ignorance here in Britain. My first point of contact will be the woman I met at the protest. Then, I will use my connections at the newspaper to bring the story to light. It's my purpose to inform the world of the vile tribalism and abuse of power that has been perpetuated by the Nigerian soldier. And all of it, perpetrated within the flawed system left after British colonial settlement.

I want you to know that I'm not giving up on our friendship because of a slight conflict and I'm certainly not letting the Asaba massacre see a fate of forget, neglect, and omission. I won't be able to leave this Earth knowing that the future generations to come, particularly Nigerians, are liable to forget the unique ambivalence that the people of Asaba possessed during the civil war. My reasons for doing this, as with yours, are not based on bitterness and vengeance but are rather rooted in the desire to honour and commemorate all who have lost their lives as a result of it.

Onome

14th May 1968

Dear Diary,

It has been almost two months but I haven't had the time to write my thoughts down since February 19th. It is still hard to process the anger I felt that day.

I initially thought that upon getting the newspaper I would rush into my flat and search through it immediately. But the suspense that had been built up surrounding this newspaper somehow caused me to be nervous and tread carefully. I sat on my bed for about ten minutes without having even opened the newspaper. Intrusive thoughts raced through my mind. Imagine if Kate lied about Asaba being mentioned in the article? After all, she seemed very secretive about the entire situation. Had I been through all this struggle only to find nothing inside the newspaper? I remember having to close my curtains because there was a black cat sitting on my external windowsill. I refused to have a cat staring at me with such intensity whilst I uncovered the truth about Asaba.

I opened the newspaper and began to delve, searching for anything related to Nigeria. When I reached the page, I noticed that there was an article on the Nigerian Civil War. I subconsciously let out a loud scream. As I read through the article, I saw that there was indeed a mention of Asaba, describing the atmosphere in Asaba as 'calm' and claiming that many civilians are returning to clean their homes. My body started to shake at the thought of their censorship of the shooting, raping, and looting done by the federal troops as Chioma had mentioned. What I found even more suspicious was that the *Daily Times* made a reference to Asaba at all, given how small the town is. British newspapers usually only cover areas such as Lagos, Abuja, and Kaduna, even in such a turbulent time of civil war. I began to suspect that the *Daily Times* might've mentioned Asaba to reduce any form of suspicion from the public. The notion that the army of Britain's former colony has behaved in such a disorderly manner would prove disruptive and detrimental to Britain's public view globally. It all made perfect sense to me. The British press are deliberately and intentionally partaking in the censorship of the

59

Asaba massacre. This kind of censorship is not only being carried out by the British, but the Nigerian government has plenty to answer for. I do recall when Chioma told me about how the Nigerian government was fighting to ensure that the news of the Asaba massacre didn't spread and that speaking about it has become taboo.

Reading the article infuriated me to such a level that it became hard for me to contain my emotions. My disgust caused my face to tighten and my body to shake. After I had examined the contents of the newspaper article, I cut it out and put it inside my drawer. The drawer that was initially intended to be a place for nostalgic items that remind me of home became a storage box for evidence. I scanned the various memories inside. The brown bead took me back to my third month in London when I decided to go to Brixton to get my hair braided. An old receipt sparked a vivid recollection of when I fried plantain during my first October in London to celebrate Nigerian Independence Day. These memories, these places, so important to me.

My little investigation doesn't stop here. Only reading the *Daily Times* isn't enough. I need to read articles from other newspaper companies to find out if they happen to mention Asaba too. It would be unfair for me to judge all the newspaper companies in Britain to hold the same values as the *Daily Times*. Once I have those to hand, I can compare the different perspectives and agendas pertaining to the events in Asaba. Only then will I be able to see the British press making a conscious effort to censor the Asaba massacre, making it my sole duty to bring the authentic story forward. I need to find the woman at the protest. Though I'm puzzled about where to look I might have found a pathway to her.

This morning I thought to myself that she had to be a student at King's College because she participated in a protest that was organised by the global social justice society. Though she looked significantly older than an undergraduate student. Nevertheless, she must've been an active member of the society. My old friend Abena, an international student from Ghana, has previously spoken about the different social events she has attended hosted

61

by the global social justice society. Abena and I aren't as close as Kate and me. Abena is studying a different degree from us and, dare I say it, our friendship was initially due to convenience. We both helped each other navigate the racially homogeneous campus.

I gave Abena a call and she sounded ecstatic to hear from me. It had been over half a year since we last spoke to each other. She told me all about an English boy she met in one of her lectures and how they began dating. But, after the racist heckling they had received in public, Abena felt that it was best to end the relationship. Ironically, her reasoning for doing so was not due to the racism but due to her partner's overly bothered reaction to it. Abena has dated several white men in the past, so she had adapted to the entitlement that the British people had to comment on her romances. It was disappointing to hear. I suggested that we meet up in person, hinting at a global social justice society event. Enthusiastically, she told me that they have a quiz session coming up in a few months. It will be focused on Africa, the first of its kind.

8. Chioma

17th June 1968

Dear Onome,

I admire your ability to acknowledge your wrongs. I might've been quite harsh on you in my previous letter, but I was very emotional at the time. I felt that you deserved to know exactly how I felt. Not a sugar-coated version that did not fully express my disappointment. Critical thinking is a quality of yours that I respect to the fullest. Your brain works so differently to mine, but our conflicting ideas make us such a cohesive unit. Your interest in the Daily Times newspaper article made me very anxious, not because I thought you were investigating it critically but because I feared that you were simply reading too much into it. Little did I know that your interest was based on the need to understand why the British were undermining the legitimacy of the Asaba massacre in order to make adequate claims against their rife censorship. You're certainly one of a kind Onome!

You're completely correct. We need to work together whilst making the best out of our individual situations in order to inform the public about the Asaba massacre. I should be able to interview some people in David's village. The only issue with that is that I'll need to let him know some details about our plan. He has done so much for me by providing me shelter and sending my letters. Though I was hesitant to tell him, I think it might be a smart idea right now. News on the street is that Nigeria is increasing levels of censorship. I sincerely believe that letters could either stop being sent to Britain, or the contents will be heavily searched for secessionist sympathisers. So, if I told David about our discussions, I would hope that he wouldn't willingly let an outsider or potential enemy read the contents of my letter before sending it off. That would be disastrous for us all. I have learnt a lot from Femi as you can probably gauge from the mere tone of my words. I am constantly searching for ways to prevent suspicion.

David and Femi need to be aware of our plan, I think they could both be great assets in executing it. Though we'll be at the forefront of it,

David's connections with the diaspora are necessary and Femi's previous experience serving in the Nigerian army can help us to understand the brutality in Asaba and predict any potential enemies. As a team, we could challenge the censorship at the hands of the British and Nigerian governments respectively. Perhaps if you find that woman from the protest then she could also join us. A huge risk with these decisions is trust. There is always a slight possibility that one of them will expose our plans. But I genuinely don't believe that they would. If we're working as a team, then from now on we must make decisions together.

You should investigate the actions of the British press further. I am in full support of your ideas. The only thing that causes me concern is that your support officer might suspect your intentions. Therefore, I think it's safest if you take a more subtle approach to your investigation as we do not want to put our plan in jeopardy.

The last part of your letter not only brought a smile to my face but also a tear to my eye. Inside I knew that you would come to your senses, but I was

65

worried for a while that London was changing you as a person. I am so thankful that that is not the case. Finally, in response to your question, I am in!

Chioma

24th June 1968

Dear Diary,

I am broken. I am hurt. I know to trust nobody and fear everybody. All I can do is thank God that I've freed myself from those evil people.

This morning, I handed David yet another one of my letters to Onome. David usually asks for my letters on Monday mornings before he leaves for work, selling paintings at the local market. The means by which David sent my letters was always a curiosity of mine. I dared not question him as I knew what his response would be. He would question my hypocrisy of trusting him enough to live under his roof but suspect him when he sends my letters to Onome. He won't hesitate to remind me that it's a favour that he does, free of charge.

Nevertheless, I was persistent in knowing whether the letters would be safe. David said his goodbyes before he left for work and placed my letter in the front pocket of his brown bookbag. At the sound of the door shutting, I ran upstairs to check that Femi was still asleep. His door, which tends to squeak at any touch, was slightly ajar so I made light steps towards it and peeked through the hole only to find Femi fast asleep. His arms and legs were spread out like a starfish, perfectly undisturbed. I darted back downstairs, opened the front door and ran after David.

The neighbourhood is relatively quiet and there tend to only be a handful of people outside in the early hours of the morning, so it was easy enough to find David rounding the corner at the end of the road. I sprinted after him, staying just out of view behind the lines of houses. As he walked down the street he stopped in the middle of the road and waited. He stood there for several minutes, making no motion to continue. I was confused, especially as he kept looking around as though he were expecting to see somebody.

Eventually, a tall, dark-skinned man in army attire approached David. Just by his appearance alone, I was sure that he was a Hausa man working in the Nigerian army. He might've even been one of the savages who massacred people at the welcome ceremony. My heart skipped a beat, and I began to contemplate whether to run back home or continue spying. I tried to move but my legs remained planted on the dusty ground. As much as I wanted to put my own safety first, I worried for David. After everything he had done for me, I needed to confirm that he was safe. I felt guilty that he was in possession of a letter that could get him killed.

The road was extremely empty, so the soldier immediately saw David and made his way toward him. David stood completely still. The soldier came about a metre away from David and David moved back into a small bush and the soldier followed him. Both looked around suspiciously and I continued to disguise myself behind the nearest house. David reached into his bookbag and brought out my letter. I couldn't believe my eyes. My letter. The very man that I had trusted to send my handwritten letters to Onome had just willingly given it to a soldier. A soldier part of the very unit that tormented my people and was likely holding my younger brother hostage. The very establishment that had prevented me from returning to my home! The soldier didn't ask further questions or proceed to search David. He simply placed the letter in his pocket and walked back in the same direction he came.

David had been deceiving me the whole time. Now I doubt that Onome has even been reading any of my letters at all. I was so foolish for believing that it was Onome that I was conversing with! David was probably writing Onome's responses to save time whilst the federal government launched an investigation against me!

I knew I was not safe in that place. David had been plotting against me the entire time and now the federal government was most likely aware of my plans. I might get arrested and suffer a similar fate to Wole Soyinka. I should've left as soon as Femi told me that he was once a Nigerian soldier. Why did I feel compelled to trust that he was a righteous person?

All these thoughts and questions overwhelmed me, and I lost my senses. I stumbled and fell into the arms of a stranger. It was a male voice calling my name, asking what I was doing out here and if I was alright. The voice sounded incredibly familiar but as my body shut down, I couldn't make out who it was straight away. A breeze of warm, stuffy air rushed into my face, and I squinted and slightly opened my eyes. The man who had caught me was David.

I tried to fight myself out of his arms, screaming that he was a traitor and demanding to get my belongings and leave. His face changed from worry to fury. Instead of letting me go, David was angry that I was following him, completely disregarding the fact that he betrayed me. His deep voice broke like someone who has been lied to by the one they trusted the most, which infuriated me. I didn't think David would depict himself as a victim even though he knows that I saw him giving my letter to that federal soldier. David backed away from me, finally releasing me from his tight grip. His face reversed from a look of fury to worry again, his cursing turning to pleading. He told me that the federal soldier was his friend, Joseph, who was helping him send my letters. He assured me that he isn't a federal soldier and is just disguised as one to avoid detection. What a lousy excuse. I wondered if he just came up with it on the spot, it was so weak. I chose not to respond and turned away, wanting nothing more than to leave.

It was then that David told me that he has news that he wouldn't be able to forgive himself if he didn't tell me. He looked me straight in the eyes and said that my brother Chukwuemeka was killed the day of the massacre. Apparently, he had asked Joseph to look into the case and he confirmed his death. At the sound of Chukwuemeka, I stopped in my tracks and turned to face David. He was lying. There was no way that Chukwuemeka was killed that day and it was from this 'Joseph' that I was finding out. A warm tear trickled from my left eye as the anger boiled inside of me.

He was a wicked man for using Chukwuemeka to try and convince me of his honesty. I looked him straight in his eyes and opened my mouth to speak but words didn't come out. I let out a small cry and whispered that God will punish him. Within a blink of an eye, I sprinted down the road to collect my belongings and began my journey home. I didn't care what was waiting for me there, for all I wanted to know was the truth. Whether or not Chukwuemeka was alive. David didn't even come running after me.

Now, I'm camped by a tree, on the way home. I physically can't carry my two heavy bags all the way there without taking a break. After I've written this diary entry my journey continues. I'll admit that a tiny part of me wonders vainly about the possibility of David telling the truth. Is it fair for me to leave Onome uninformed of this huge decision I am making? But surely it wasn't truly Onome who was writing to me all this time if I have just witnessed David giving my letter to a stranger working in the Nigerian army? God free me from these unwanted doubts!

I may have felt that Onome was just a letter away from Asaba. But realistically, she is hundreds of miles away and I'm certain that those letters were not from her.

9. Onome

4th August 1968

Dear Chioma,

I'm ecstatic that you're willing to collaborate with me on this secret project to find and report the truth about Asaba. I would like to reiterate the word 'secret' because though I do believe in your judgement regarding David and Femi, I think that it's too soon to be informing people of it. You barely even know them. I understand that you have all been living under the same roof for almost a year now so that would have intensified your experience of getting to know each other, but it's too soon to be giving them the keys to our kingdom. Though we could largely benefit from David's vast connections and Femi's military expertise, I'm not willing to risk sabotaging our plan for two men whom we may not be able to fully trust.

But you, Chioma, are a necessity to this plan. I'm extremely excited that you have decided to stand by me with this decision. Yes, it'll be difficult doing something behind the backs of the people that helped you in a time of desperate need. But do not think about it like that! That's not the case at all. You're simply doing them both a favour without letting them know. It's quite an act of humility if you ask me. You're simply working to give the people of Asaba a voice. Once we have achieved what we set out to do then we can reveal ourselves as the pioneers of this project. It mustn't be forgotten that you're already putting all of you in that household in danger but letting them know about the insides and outsides of our plan will only cast them into even more risk.

However, strangely enough, I agree with your idea to talk to David about the contents of our letters. We still don't know exactly how he is sending these letters; suppose one day he was stopped by a government official, it's important that he remains sharp and aware of the danger. Whilst you shouldn't go into detail about our conversations, just tell him that you're in contact with a friend in London about the situation in Asaba. Make it clear that your friend has promised not to speak of anything that you have told them out of respect for the federal government's demands.

On my part, I will make striving efforts to drive the process of revealing the truth about Asaba. I agreed to meet an old friend, Abena, to attend a global social justice society event. I am hoping to see the woman at the protest there since the protest was organised by the global social justice society. I don't exactly remember how she looks, but once I see her face again, I'm confident that I'll be able to recognise her. Her look of deep sorrow lingers in my mind.

Chioma, please take care. Though I stand firm in my belief that we ought to leave Femi and David out of this, do not be afraid to follow your heart on what you think is right to do for the sake of the two of us.

Onome

<u>Part 2.</u>

3 months later

10. Onome

1st November 1968

Dear Diary,

It's winter and the civil war persists. From what I've read in the newspapers available to us here in Britain I reckon that the circumstances in Biafra are dreadful. I am quite surprised that the Biafrans are still fighting and that General Ojukwu has not attempted to negotiate an armistice. The embargo placed on Biafra by the Federal Government is beginning to push Biafra to the brink of defeat. Horrible images of young children with kwashiorkor are starting to surface within the press. Everyone within my department and related fields are talking about the civil war. It was once seen as a minor war as many were confident that the federal government would secure a swift victory over the Biafrans, especially given the vast support from Britain. But the Biafrans have fought surprisingly well and organised.

Every day I give praise to God for enabling Chioma to send me those letters. She risked her life to share a story that had been neglected and censored. I have not heard from her at all for the past three months and miss reading her words, gaining an insight into her life back in Asaba, and just knowing that she is safe. I think about her every hour of each day. But as she once told me that she did not lament too much for Chukwuemeka when he was missing, I too don't want to think about her too much lest I spiral.

Chukwuemeka passed away on the day of the massacre. I received the news from Chioma's great Aunt Amaka who gave me a spontaneous call not too long after I stopped hearing from Chioma. I assume that's why I haven't heard from her in a while. She needs time to mourn the death of her younger and only brother. It would be selfish of me to bombard her with letters at such a sensitive and sorrowful time. Great Aunty Amaka sounded devastated on the telephone. From the mere tone of her voice, I could tell that she had been crying for days. I asked her if I could speak to Chioma and told her that I hadn't received a letter from her lately, but she informed me that she saw Chioma the other day and that she was moving to Lagos to be with her parents. So, I'm forced to wait for her to write when she's ready.

Sometimes I wonder why Chioma didn't stay with Aunty Amaka in Asaba. Aunty Amaka is one of the wealthiest members of her family. A great woman who refuses to live abroad, or in larger cities like Lagos despite being able to afford to. "Why would I want to live in London only to be working a low-wage job and facing racial discrimination on a daily basis?" was what she would always say when I visited her with Chioma. Aunty Amaka does not idolise the white man and his treasures. I wish more Nigerians had a similar mindset to her. Had Chioma stayed with Aunty Amaka then we would've been able to call each other occasionally because she would then be able to afford it. Now that she has moved all the way to Lagos where censorship is even more potent than in Asaba I probably won't be hearing from her for a long while. But all in all, I'm glad that she is back with her family as now that Chukwuemeka is gone there is nobody left in her childhood home. Living alone in that house would only increase her grief.

During our conversation, Aunty Amaka told me that Chioma's parents had changed their names to Yoruba ones in Lagos to avoid attacks. I assume that Chioma followed in their footsteps when she travelled to Lagos. I cannot imagine how it would feel to be forced into changing your birth name. When I think of the act of stripping one's identity for the purpose of genocide or eradicating an ethnic group, I think of the transatlantic slave trade in the American South. But now my thoughts drift to Nigeria, which is disgraceful. A country consisting of vibrant cultures and intelligent individuals has adopted the strategies of the slave masters.

My inability to speak to Chioma is like a wound in my gut. I wish I could hear her voice or read her words. I wish I could tell her that I was finally able to find the woman from the protest. The very woman that we were discussing in our letters. The woman we thought had all the answers.

My decision to give Abena a call was well thought out. I did attend the quiz night as we had discussed prior. It was an intriguing experience and though my main purpose of attending was to try and find the woman, I was enjoying the event so much that I forgot about it. I found her when I least expected to. One of the questions during the quiz was to point out the correct map of Biafra. There were four different options, two of which were evidently false. The other two were plausible options for someone who was not too educated on the war. One was the correct map and the other one included parts of Bendel State, so places like Asaba and Warri were considered part of Biafra. As expected only a few of us got the question correct. Even Abena was wrong as she chose the one that included parts of Bendel State. Some were even so misguided as to choose one that had shaded only the Northern region of Nigeria. I couldn't help but let out a grin when the results were announced. But I noticed how irritated a woman in the corner of the room looked. She raised her hand and the teacher indicated that she could speak. She openly criticised the insensitivity of the question given the recent Asaba massacre that occurred. That Asaba is not part of Biafra yet the people had to suffer as a result of the war. Hardly anybody took notice of what she said, but I recognised her voice. It was the woman I had been searching for.

After the quiz, I made sure to seek out the woman, whose name was Ruth. Getting the chance to speak with her was a breath of fresh air. She was so educated and confident in her beliefs. The very fact that she could raise her opinions against one of the quiz questions in front of a large crowd already confirmed that. Ruth is a postgraduate student who studies medicine at King's College London. She is from Asaba and was offered a generous scholarship to pursue further studies. I'm not surprised in the slightest that she was able to obtain such a competitive offer. Ruth has the unique ability to delve into topics that otherwise go unnoticed and share the information without fearing that others will not be able to relate or comprehend.

After the quiz, we exchanged numbers and kept in contact. We met regularly at cafes to discuss the massacre. Just as it was the only thing that I couldn't stop thinking about, for Ruth, it was the only thing keeping her up at night. Our similarities of interest soon blossomed into a lovely friendship. One that I cherish months later. Had I not seen her at the protest and learnt of the massacre from Chioma, we would have probably never crossed paths. I am not usually one to step outside of my comfort zone and the act of building a friendship with a woman much older than me pursuing a master's degree was quite daunting. But her life experiences have been so crucial in forming our bond and shared desire to share the story of the Asaba massacre with the rest of the world.

Ruth told me everything. From the story of how her friend, a man called Maduka, had been killed in the massacre. She was told by his mother who had witnessed the whole incident and who was later subjected to rape by the soldiers. Our conversation was very gruesome, and I couldn't help but cry. I felt then that it was only right for me to show her my letters from Chioma. I took the letters everywhere I went, kept safe in a large brown envelope. I took the large envelope out of my book bag and handed it to her. Ruth opened the envelope and as she read, I watched her intensively. I analysed her facial expressions as her eyes scanned the pages from left to right. Her facial expressions were varied, at times she looked happy and at other times she wore a look of despair.

After Ruth read through my lengthy correspondences with Chioma, she sat in silence for a moment. Following a minute's pause, she dried her throat and thanked me for sharing such a personal aspect of my life with her. I reflected on the word 'personal'. For me, Chioma and my letters were not personal. They were important and needed to be shared with others. Suddenly my mind drifted back to the argument that I had with Chioma, our discussions about Chukwuemeka, and most importantly the infamous "Britain changed you". I realised that our letters did indeed contain personal matters. Would Chioma have even appreciated that our intimate thoughts on her deceased brother were shared with Ruth?

Ruth initially was not too keen on my blooming idea to discuss my letters with my support officer at the *Daily Times*. According to her, to take down the enemy you must disguise your agenda. Ruth suggested that I instead try and get access to other newspaper articles that referred to the Asaba massacre at my internship. She pointed out that, as an intern, I possess rich access to articles from different companies and could possibly carry out a subtle investigation during my work breaks. The only barrier I faced was Peter, my support officer.

11. Chioma

2nd November 1968

Dear Diary,

I know that I've abandoned you for a while. The last time I wrote was the day I left David's. I was in a dark place and was too stubborn to tell you all that has been happening. But now, I feel like there's nobody that I can talk to. Chukwuemeka was once that person that I could confide in, but he is gone.

After I left David's, a large part of me could sense that trouble was near. The walk to Aunty Amaka's place was dreadful. Not only was I carrying heavy luggage, but thoughts were also racing through my mind. I initially wanted to set out to find Chukwuemeka, but I quickly figured that if anyone was to know about his whereabouts it would be Aunty Amaka. She is one of the only family members that I have left in Asaba. I was having petrifying thoughts about what could've happened that day. I was getting visions of bullet wounds and large rifle guns. It was honestly horrifying. By the time I reached Aunty Amaka's, my legs were incredibly sore, not only from walking but from the emotional weight of it all.

Aunty Amaka was shocked to see me. I suppose that's quite understandable given that I had left my family in the dark about my plans to reside in a stranger's house for a year. I had told them that I was safe but did not give them much information about where I was staying. Though I had tried to send messages to my parents through David's 'so-called' contacts, I never really requested to know whether they had received them.

But one thing that David didn't lie about was Chukwuemeka's death. As soon as I walked into Aunty Amaka's compound she greeted me with a warm and long hug. Through her touch, I knew something was wrong. She then told me how worried she was about me and thought that I had suffered the same fate as Chukwuemeka. It was then that the truth hit me, sharper than a knife. I dropped to my knees and began to weep. I blamed myself for his death. Femi, David, and even Onome pressured me to remain hopeful when I should have been yearning to get to the bottom of what happened to

Chukwuemeka. My first mistake was following Femi when I should've been looking out for my brother. My cowardly act cost him his life. As I feel betrayed by David and Femi, he too must have felt deeply betrayed by me after watching my faint-hearted escape. David and Femi's treachery was understandable. I'd only known them for less than a year, so they owed me no loyalty. But growing up, Chukwuemeka always looked up to me. If he ever needed help with anything or needed somebody to speak with after having a tough day, he would turn to me. He looked to me for comfort and guidance. Despite having caring parents, our similarity in age meant that I could relate to his issues. At times our parents were ignorant to certain difficulties that the youth face in Nigeria. The moment that that federal soldier grabbed him viciously by the arm was the moment that I should have stepped up to fulfil my role as his older sister.

That day I failed to protect Chukwuemeka, and I should rightfully hold myself accountable. Instead of running away from the scene with Femi, I should have ensured that he was safe. That the soldiers didn't cause him any harm. I still wonder why I was so certain that he would be allowed to leave or, in the worst case be enlisted. I cannot even imagine how helpless he must've felt at that time. I would imagine that he would've looked to me for guidance and protection but didn't find me as I was too busy running away through the bushes. Then for me to stay in a stranger's house for such a long time without making any kind of effort to locate Chukwuemeka was even worse. I will never forgive myself for the way I behaved.

After some days of mourning and grief, I had to start piecing my life back together. I quickly realised that I was in deep danger. If David had given my letter to a soldier, then that man had most certainly read through it by now. Because of this, I am a serious threat to the Nigerian government, especially with my connections to Onome. Her safety might even be at risk too. I decided that for my own safety, it was best for me to relocate to Lagos to be with my parents. Aunty Amaka was confused as to why I was so persistent to move which is understandable as she isn't aware of the context of our letters. But I told her that I wished to be with my immediate family during this harsh time.

This is partly true, but I cannot deny how influential the potential exposure of my letters has been to my decision to depart. As much as I am saddened by the death of Chukwuemeka, I am fearful that I too can lose my life at such a young age. My parents would be devastated to lose both of us. I haven't made them aware of my plans with Onome and that the government is probably aware of it. The least I can do is spend quality time with them whilst I'm still alive. During my short stay with Aunty Amaka, I remembered that my parents had told me about how they had changed their names to Yoruba ones to avoid confrontation with authority. My mother's changed from Nnenna to Adeola whereas my father's went from Okorie to Adeboye. It's a bitter reality for Igbo people in this current climate. I'm someone who takes pride in my name which means 'God is good'. So, it wasn't an easy decision for me to make but I felt that it was necessary. Though I was proud of being called Chioma and coming from Asaba, it was crucial for me to put my safety first.

In order to maintain my friendship with Onome I knew that I had to stop writing letters to her. I was aware of how hard it would be, but it was necessary to keep her safe. If the federal soldiers cannot come for me then they might turn to her. I've already lost Chukwuemeka due to my selfishness, I cannot now lose Onome. I cannot make the same mistake. That is why I am so grateful that I can share my thoughts in this diary. For I am forced to conceal these thoughts in order to protect others.

12. Onome

4th November 1968

Dear Diary,

This morning I made my way to the office at the *Daily Times*. I had to wear my thick brown jacket as the days are rainy and cold and the harsh winter times are slowly starting to appear as November passes by. As I made my way through the front doors, I glanced at the staff room to my left and there was an array of newspapers, mostly from the *Daily Times* but also a section dedicated to external newspapers. I began to regret spending all my lunch breaks flicking through *Things Fall Apart* by Chinua Achebe instead of searching for evidence buried within those newspapers.

Peter was in a remarkably cheerful mood today. As soon as I entered the office I was greeted with a warm smile. He told me about my tasks for the day. I had some research to do on the current events of the Vietnam war but during my break, I made my way to the staff room and approached the

93

cabinet with the newspapers. I picked up a few from the *Daily Times* and as I tried to pull the handle to get one of the external newspapers the cabinet wouldn't open. It didn't bulge in the slightest. I was so confused as to why they kept the other newspapers locked up. As my eyes met the bottom right-hand corner, I saw a small key lock with no key. I needed that key. I had to speak with Peter.

I headed back to the office, butterflies in my stomach. I was nervous to ask Peter for something so normal. For all he cared, I could've just been interested in reading different newspapers. But my intentions behind asking were causing me such anxiety. Peter was sitting at his desk with his glasses on, reading an article of some sort. When he saw me, he removed his glasses and raised his bushy eyebrows. I managed to stutter a request to read some of the other newspapers in the cabinet. Peter looked surprised but didn't question me further. He opened it up, telling me that the reason the papers were locked away in the first place was that they were all from our competitors. He didn't want to waste money buying multiple copies, so he kept them locked up during the day in case they were used for scrap. I felt slightly guilty, knowing that I would happily cut up one of the newspapers if it contained anything relevant to Asaba.

I decided to take a *Daily Sketch* newspaper, recognising it as a conservative publication. Luckily, I was the only person in the staff room so I could search through it at my leisure. I opened the newspaper and started to go through each article in chronological fashion. Most of the stories seemed to be domestically inclined with hyperbolic headlines. As I flicked further, I saw "Nigeria" written clearly in bold font. I gently placed my fingers on the page to flatten out the paper. There was no mention of Asaba in the article. I raised my eyes to the clock on the wall and saw that there were only five minutes left until Peter expected me to be back in the office. On the spur of the moment, I decided to take the newspaper home.

Kate has invited me to dinner tonight; I am going over after work. I feel guilty. We have barely spoken over the past few weeks. But this morning, she invited me to her house. Not her student flat, but her large family home in Harrow. It must be splendid to have the luxury of living in the same city that you study in. I've always wondered why Kate didn't decide to just live at home for the duration of her degree. It would save her a lot of money as the cost of flats in the city is extremely expensive. But I supposed that she was wealthy enough to decide whether she wants to live at home.

As I'm writing this, I'm waiting in the *Daily Times* reception to be picked up by Kate's father. Writing eases off my nerves and I'm so nervous to meet this man. I don't even know why.

13. Chioma

18th December 1968

Dear Onome,

It's been a while since we last spoke and I deeply apologise for leaving you in the dark about my absence. It hasn't been easy for me as I'm sure you know. Not so long ago I found out Chukwuemeka was killed during the massacre. Perhaps you're already aware of this because Aunty Amaka did tell me that she'd try and get in contact with you, even though I begged her not to. A lot has happened since I last wrote to you and though I'm not going to go into detail about the exact events that have occurred, I feel as though you deserve to know why I haven't responded to your last letter. If you even received any.

I'm currently in Lagos with my parents. I left David's place some weeks ago. I had always suspected that he was untrustworthy. It didn't make sense to me how he could allow a stranger to live in his house and help them send letters to people

97

abroad in exchange for nothing. Though there are thoughtful human beings around, living in David's house felt too good to be true. Both Femi and David's attitude toward me was always too sympathetic. They pitied me all the time and looked down on me. I was forced to tailor my behaviour to fit the dynamics of the household. I must admit it was suffocating. The only thing keeping me sane was our letters.

You might be wondering why I stopped writing to you. My suspicion of David drove me to follow him to work one day. I caught him willingly giving my letter to you to a federal soldier! A man that is part of the very group that tortured the people of Asaba and even went so far as killing my own brother. Even though he convinced me that they were being sent directly to you, I could no longer trust him. That faint trust that I had for him was demolished. I don't know what to believe anymore. I don't even know whether or not it was really you responding or those evil people fabricating your responses only to distract me whilst they make plans to imprison me. So Onome, if it is really you, then confirm when and where we first met. I know if this is really you reading it you must be disheartened that I am even asking you this but I need to be fully certain. Everything thus far in our letter conversations has felt so real and inside I truly believe that it's you because I know you. But my paranoia is eating through my soul, and I need to find out the truth.

Onome, if this is really you then I want you to know that I'm in danger. I'm a lot safer in Lagos though because I have changed my name to Folake. That is the length that us Igbo people must take just to ensure that we're safe within our own country. I left Asaba because I could sense that I was unsafe, that there were people of authority in search of me. The fact that that soldier has my letter means that it's very likely that the government has read through all our letters and that leaves you in danger too. Onome, be careful of your surroundings! Our plan to reveal the truth about the federal troops in Asaba doesn't only threaten the Nigerian government and army, but also the British. That's why they're working so hard to conceal the reality of the situation. You pose a threat to them. When we eventually reveal the Asaba massacre to the general *public, other nations will condemn Britain. They will condemn Britain for arming and facilitating a reckless army in pursuit of economic interests. They will shake their heads at the British support of a wicked and heartless army that slaughters innocent civilians in the name of unity.*

Folake

14. Onome

5th November 1968

Dear Diary,

Before Kate's father picked me up, I was excited. Since embarking on my studies in London I'd barely been outside of the inner city, so I thought it'd be interesting to get to see another part of London. Though I insisted that I'd find my way there by bus, Kate firmly told me that she would get her father to collect me.

I stood and waited outside of my work building and watched all the cars drive past. I had never met Kate's father previously so I was slightly uncertain as to how he would know where exactly to collect me from. Though I did mention to Kate that I would be waiting outside my work building at half past four. A black ford drove towards me and parked right by where I was standing. A man greeted me from the driver's seat. He had a peculiar accent, one that I had not heard in London. It almost resembled a Scottish, but I decided it was likely from Northern England. I was surprised that he remembered my surname. Mister Hunt was formally dressed in a black suit and had a hat on. I associate hats with the rich. He had a similar condescending tone to his daughter. He told me that Kate couldn't make it as she was helping her mother prepare the dinner so without hesitation I got into the car and prepared for the long journey to Harrow.

I got into the back seat as I couldn't bear to sit in the front of the car with a man that I had never met before. It felt so foreign to be inside a car after over a year. Because I live near campus, I walk everywhere I go. If I need to travel a bit further outside of central London, which is quite rare, I usually take the bus or the train. I inspected the inside of the car, which was pristinely clean. The seat beside me had a stack of newspapers, a book and a pen placed on it. I began to wonder what his occupation was. Not so long ago, Kate mentioned that he was active in politics.

After a moment of silence, Mister Hunt asked how my studies were. I told him the usual, that the course was very demanding but I'm enjoying it. Once he had broken the ice he decided to ask me if I was from Nigeria. I nodded and then realised that he couldn't see me, so I let out a quick "Yes!" from the back of the car. I anxiously asked him if Kate told him that I was from Nigeria. At that point, he began to laugh. I will never fully understand the humour of the British people. They laugh at times that are least expected and remain serious during the moments that I find hilarious. Kate has indeed mentioned my Nigerian heritage, but Mister Hunt claimed that he could tell merely by my name. That Edewor is a common surname in Midwest Nigeria. I frowned a little when he told me this. How did he know so much about Nigeria? Though Kate had always listened to me speak about Nigeria, she never really spoke much about it herself, and yet her father seemed to know such particular details. It was refreshing to witness someone with an interest in my homeland.

When we finally got to Harrow, he led me to the front door and gave a firm knock. Kate came to open the door rather quickly and greeted me with a hug. As I stepped into her house Mister Hunt turned and headed back to the car. I was very confused as to why he was not staying for dinner and where he was heading to at six o'clock in the evening. But Kate told me that he had some work to do at the office. He must be very hardworking to prioritise his occupation over family dinners. I wanted to ask about his occupation, but I noticed that Kate looked rather down and so I refrained. I commiserate with how she must've felt, having a busy parent who is hardly home. It reminded me of my parents. They own a food market in Warri.

That night Kate's mother, a woman named Sarah, cooked a roast dinner. It looked quite appealing. Kate looks almost identical to her mother. Both have long brown hair with large eyes and thin lips. But their personalities differed hugely. Missus Hunt is very quiet and tender as opposed to her daughter who is assertive and potent. At their house, Missus Hunt barely spoke but she was constantly smiling at me. It was an unsettling expression, as though she either loved or hated me.

Without much conversation during dinner, I found my eyes wandering. They landed on a booklet placed on a sideboard near the dining table. The handwriting was old-fashioned and slanted. The type of writing that one would see in a diary of a man who lived centuries ago. The title of the page read "West and General Africa Department memorandum". It stood out in a house full of English people. I noticed that both Kate and Sarah were staring in my direction, so I quickly fixed my eyes back on my plate. During the rest of dinner, I couldn't stop thinking about how the paper was placed just within my reach. I had so many thoughts. What did it say? Who did it belong to? I tried to conceal my curiosity in the document, but Kate continuously looked between it and me.

After we finished eating, Kate got up out of her chair and walked towards me. I followed her movements with my eyes, and she walked right past and picked up the booklet on the sideboard to return it to a nearby bookshelf. I doubt it was coincidental. The atmosphere was unpleasant and she reeked of guilt.

15. Chioma

23rd December 1968

Dear Diary,

It has been almost a week since I sent a letter to Onome so I'm still awaiting a response. This is make or break. If I get a letter back from her then I'll know that I have been writing to her all this time. But if I don't, I've been horribly deceived. Whilst sending letters in Asaba seemed to be a prolonged and uncertain process, in Lagos it's much easier. Especially as we have all changed our names to Yoruba ones and identify as Yoruba people, my father can send my letters for me. It's quite expensive though, a pound too much to describe, probably due to the inflation caused by the war effort. Nevertheless, I prefer it that way as opposed to David. At least now I don't have to be anxious about my letters being in the hands of a federal soldier.

My parents and I are staying at a family friend's house. I don't know anything about him; all

I've been told is that he's a wealthy man who lives abroad in America so his house was empty before my parents moved in. It's a rather small place in Ikeja with just enough space to accommodate the three of us. Since my arrival, my parents have been constantly cautious and fearful of attack. I was hoping to live in their house in Lekki but they're too afraid to stay there as they fear that their Igbo names might have been tied to the place through housing registration. Their fear is palpable. My mother flinches at the sound of a door closing and my father never ceases to listen to the radio. Sometimes I wonder why I'm so composed compared to my parents. I believe it to have been my experience in Asaba last year. It has shaped my existence today. The Asaba massacre drained my heart. The last time I recall fully expressing my emotions was when I heard about Chukwuemeka's passing. But even then, I didn't respond as I usually would've, prior to the massacre.

This afternoon my father scolded me for speaking on the massacre when I asked my mother if she'd heard anything from her friends back in Asaba. He looked genuinely furious; I'd never seen

107

him like that in my entire life. I couldn't hold back my tears. I need somebody to speak to about the massacre and Onome was once that person, but my parents refuse to converse with me on the matter. Neither of them has even made an effort to gain an insight into what I experienced that day. We're yet to have a fruitful conversation about what I've experienced whilst I was away for the past year. The same taboo concerning the massacre that I felt in Asaba is present in my very household.

Personally, I reckon that they are still upset about my absconding with Femi and David. My mother often asks if I even attempted to get in contact with anybody at all. I largely regret telling her that I had been in contact with Onome because it only made her even more bitter, knowing that her only daughter had been missing for such a long period of time and willingly chose her best friend over her own mother. The truth is, I was traumatised living at David's. Traumatised by the horrific scenes that I had witnessed and traumatised about the untold and unresolved fate of Chukwuemeka. Sadly, at the time I felt that Onome was the only person I could confide in, knowing she would not judge me.

Neither of my parents truly believe me about the massacre and what I experienced. A plethora of Nigerians, including my parents, are prepared to continue living their lives without investigating the brutality displayed in Asaba in October 1967. My father claims that there are unanswered questions but has not shown any eagerness to seek answers, whether it be now or after the civil war. Even though they lost their only son due to the impunity of the Nigerian soldiers, there is little to no yearning for justice.

Their reaction only solidifies why I was so quick to reach out to Onome instead of them. Their judgmental and unbothered nature is causing aches all over my body. I cannot bear to listen to their ignorance. The longer I look at them, the more I find it hard to recognise them. Are these really the parents who raised me to be patriotic and proud of my heritage? The very parents who advocated for equality and justice after experiencing colonialism? Parents who were part of the generation of Nigerians who stood up to the colonial masters and achieved our independence in 1960 when I was a young girl?

As I'm writing this, I'm sunk into a corner in my bedroom cradling my bent legs. I miss Onome more than ever before. I need to hear from her otherwise I don't know how long I'll last in this place. Oh God! Oh, Heavenly Father! Bring Onome back to me!

16. Onome

31st January 1969

Dear Folake,

I am so very sorry about your brother's passing. My sister, don't ever apologise again for rightfully mourning the loss of your brother. Having heard such dreadful news, I would never expect you to continue pursuing our plan as though nothing has happened. Please extend my condolences to your parents. I think your decision to move was a smart one; you often don't prioritise your well-being so I'm glad that you see it fitting to do so now. The news of his passing only made me more eager to uncover the truth about Asaba. He cannot die in vain. I will not allow it to happen.

Whilst I appreciate your help and will always acknowledge your bravery in even telling me about what happened in Asaba, it's now down to me to orchestrate this plan. You planted the seed and started the process by opening up to me about what you've been through, but my location enables me to

111

do more than you can at the moment. I am not restricted by civil war, nor am I facing severe censorship (though I am reading it in the press here). It is now my turn to sail our ship to victory.

You speak of David as an untrustworthy man and I'm quite perplexed as to why you would think so. Though I've had my doubts about the sincerity of both Femi and David I know that they were at least true in sending your letters. My responses are proof of that. I have received every single one of your letters and it's me replying, nobody else. You say that you would like to conduct a proof of identity examination on me. How we met, you ask? Easy question. We met in primary one at age five. We were complete opposites. Whilst I was shy, you were outgoing. You used your confidence to include me which I'll be everlastingly grateful for.

Now that you're aware that it is me and not some kind of traitor, I want you to forget the false idea that David has been lying to you. From my end, it seems that he has been loyally sending all your letters so if you blatantly accuse him and he is indeed innocent it might prompt him to investigate the contents of our letters, or even worse, tell someone about it which will then put you in more severe danger. I'm not fully disputing your suspicion as it is strange that he gave our letters to a federal soldier. But have you thought that it might be a good friend of his or even a trustworthy federal soldier helping him? Sending letters abroad is reserved for the elite in a turbulent time like this. He must have some form of connection to the army or government to be allowed to send letters. He was not honest about his means of sending your letters, but didn't he tell you that it was a complicated and secretive process? So, he didn't exactly lie? For if he were to tell you the entire truth then that would put you at risk.

Whilst you were away, I did find someone who sustained my perseverance on our quest. I was finally able to find the woman at the protest, Ruth. I attended an event hosted by the global social justice society and there she was. I couldn't identify her immediately as she had changed her hair. She no longer had braids with beads, this time she had her natural afro tied up in a bright yellow headscarf. What drew my attention was her public disapproval of one of the quiz questions which included an *incorrect, though intendedly so, map of Biafra which included Bendel state, our state. She asserted how it was insensitive to include after the Asaba massacre that had recently occurred. She brought up the massacre in front of all the students and staff that were present that day! Though it was brushed away like dust and nobody acknowledged what she said. I deeply regret not speaking up in support of our sister and found her later to tell her as much. Since that day, Ruth has been helping me with our quest.*

Your doubts about Kate were precisely valid. I met her father, a stern man named David Hunt. Though being in his presence felt quite intimidating, I was impressed by how well-informed he was about Nigeria. My sister, can you believe that he was able to distinguish my surname as not only a Nigerian one but one that is from the midwestern region? As for Kate, I'm unsure about her true intentions. Whilst I was in her house, I saw a paper that was titled "West and General Africa Department Memorandum", though Kate swiftly tried to block my gaze from the paper. I must find out what she's hiding because it could be linked to

114

Asaba. This could explain why she was so defensive about the massacre and instead pushed the false narrative given by the Daily Times.

Onome

3rd February 1969

Dear Diary,

One of the things I really appreciate about Ruth is how much she cares about her hair. The first time I saw her at the protest, she wore her hair in braids with beads. At the quiz event, it was in its natural state wrapped in a high bun. When I met her today with a cup of coffee in her hand and a bright smile, she had it in a fully blown afro. As I gazed at her hair, I could see how well-defined her natural curl pattern was. I can imagine her washing it regularly and applying oils that were sent to her straight from Nigeria every morning after she wakes up and every night before she goes to sleep.

I handed her the newspaper that I illegally acquired from my workplace, and she took it, placed it on the table, and stared at it for a while. I was so determined that she wouldn't find anything at all because there was no mention of Asaba in the slightest. I guided her to the right page, and she began to read. She made me wait a while to hear her verdict; she must've read the article three or four times, her face becoming more and more saddened. Finally, she told me this: "Onome, the British are doing all in their power to suppress the Asaba massacre and the lengths of their efforts are starting to scare me." Ruth handed me the newspaper and pointed to a specific part of the article. I read it and it said, "the federal troops have made a triumphant advance in the Midwest".

Initially, I was confused and then I received a burst of reality that rushed through my lungs. Three main points characterised their censorship. Asaba is in the Midwestern region of Nigeria. 'Triumphant advance' is painting the federal soldiers as heroic. There is no mention of the impunity perpetrated against the people of Asaba.

I dug into my bookbag and grabbed a pair of scissors and cut out the article so that I could place it in my evidence storage when I got home. I couldn't believe that I didn't realise that that implicit, yet explicit comment was made. I was so immersed in locating the word "Asaba" that I failed to delve into the words within the text. Ruth is so integral to our quest. She could so easily identify that that reference pertained to undermining the situation in Asaba. I wish I could tell her about the document that I found at Kate's and her instant shift in behaviour once she became aware of my side-glances full of curiosity. But I must first find out why.

I already slightly regret showing Ruth all our letters. Though she has helped me tremendously by providing context to my perceived uncertainties, our letters were deep and intimate. Chioma shared aspects of her life that she didn't even tell her parents and in the same breath, I told her my own secrets. From the missing status of Chukwuemeka to the rift in our friendship caused by Kate and the infamous *Daily Times* newspaper. Ruth has read through it all. Until I get concrete approval from Chioma to fully include Ruth in our plans I feel as though it's only right that I don't tell her every detail about my findings unless necessary. I hope in doing this I am not wasting valuable time. Nevertheless, that is the loyalty that I bear to Chioma.

As for Kate and me, our friendship hasn't been the same since that night. We hardly speak to each other and when we do there is an unspoken tension wavering around the air that surrounds us. Just yesterday she came to my flat to collect a pair of earrings that she had left on my windowsill the last time she visited. We barely even looked at one another and neither of us made any sort of attempt to indulge in conversation. Kate looked neither jolly nor troubled but merely had a bland expression on her face.

It was that day that I received a notice from David, my support officer, that a newspaper from the *Daily Sketch* was missing from the cabinet and that I'm the last person who gained access to the newspapers. He wondered if I'd seen it when I was looking through the newspapers, hinting that if I didn't see it then he must report it missing and open an investigation concerning the matter. I denied seeing the newspaper to avoid further questioning but a small part of me is worried that I've lit a fuse. It's too late for me to return it because I've already cut out the article and placed it inside my drawer of evidence. Additionally, I don't have the keys to the cabinet to even consider returning it. I would've never imagined that a newspaper would cause so much anxiety and chaos at my workplace. My decision to take it that day might prove to be costly, should they open an investigation.

17. Chioma

10th March 1969

Dear Onome,

I thank God for you, and I thank God for your presence in my life. You're the only light in this darkened life of mine. The only source of hope that strengthens me to remain calm and optimistic about the fate of Asaba.

I knew all along that it was you. From the mere tone of your words and sharpness of your articulation of thoughts, I was fully convinced. Asking you to confirm your identity was a necessity for me at the time. After catching David giving away my letter to you to an unknown federal soldier I began to spiral. I questioned everything, including your letters back to me. I now think back and burst into laughter at the thought of doubting the truthfulness of the words I was reading.

However, please understand why I felt that way. I now associate Nigerian soldiers with deceit, violence and recklessness. I never thought to

121

consider that David's letter operation must involve a level of fraudulency which would explain his contact with a federal soldier. He did even tell me that that federal soldier was his friend, Joseph, in disguise but I refused to believe him. I was too angered by what I had seen to begin to fathom that there was an element of truth to his claims. He might not be as untrustworthy as I've made him out to be. But there is no means of changing my perception of the soldiers fighting for unity after what I experienced in Asaba and continue to experience here in Lagos.

This time it's not being perpetuated by federal soldiers or a few strangers that I've just met but by my very own parents. I'm finding it hard to recognise them. Since they moved to Lagos, I've missed that parental presence in my life, so I was excited to come and see them and receive the comfort and love that I've been deprived of for so long. Can you believe that they refuse to speak to me about Asaba? They claim that it's too dangerous to speak about it even in our home shielded by walls. Apparently, we never know who is watching

122

or listening. It's impossible for anybody to hear us unless we are shouting at the top of our lungs.

I don't believe that that is the only reason why they do not wish to speak about it with me. I fear that the Nigerian censorship is beginning to convince them that my witness of the massacre is invalid. Even though it claimed the life of their only son. Though I sometimes hear them discussing his loss and even sometimes shedding some tears over it, there is a lack of desire to claim justice for his death. I tried to have a conversation with my mother about Asaba and my father stormed into the room demanding that I never speak of it again. I've never seen him as angry as he was in my twenty years of life. His nostrils were flaring like a bull and his body was shaking with rage.

It was at that moment that I decided that I could no longer live with my parents. The decision was sealed in my mind. My father even went so far as to tell me that I was not there for the whole duration of the massacre and so there are still many unanswered questions. Had he preferred it if I was there to witness the soldiers detaining and shooting my younger brother for my words to be believable?

123

They're attempting to convince me that I misjudged the situation in Asaba and that it was not so vile after all. The same method that the press in Britain is using to manipulate the masses into believing that Asaba is not at all involved in the conflict and that the atmosphere is 'calm' there. But the difference is the British people may have never even heard of Asaba and so one wouldn't think to question anything in the newspapers. But for my parents, it's drastically different. Asaba is their home, the town in which they were born and raised. The town they attended school in and met each other. They have so many significant memories in that small town and yet they don't care to fight for a good cause on behalf of the hundreds of civilians that were tortured in that town, including their very own son.

Onome, we must question ourselves. Might we be out of our minds thinking that we could have any sort of impact on people's views on the civil war by revealing what happened in Asaba? If sole inhabitants of Asaba are not fond of hearing what I have to say, then what does that tell us about how the rest of the world will receive our news? It is certainly something to consider. This doesn't at all mean that I'm giving up but it's just very upsetting to see. I don't seem to have a voice in my very own home so how will our voices be uplifted and positively received in a place like Britain?

On a happier note, I'm over the moon that you've finally found Ruth. I believe she will be a good ally to us, as long as you're careful about what you share. The fact that you were able to locate her in a city as big as London just shows how the Asaba massacre is destined to be shared. God knows how passionate we are about giving a voice to the unheard and so he is paving the way for us to succeed. We just need to believe that it's possible irrespective of what pessimists like my parents might think. Just imagine if I were to tell my father about our conversations, he would never allow me to send letters to you again! I'm quite surprised that he has not yet read through my letters. I don't think he reckons that I am fearless enough to talk to you about Asaba. He must think that we speak about typical topics that young women speak about like men and beauty. How naive of him!

As for Kate, didn't I tell you that she couldn't be trusted? It's such a shame because I *don't think that all English people are like that. There are many that are making striving efforts to condemn and improve the terrible actions of their English descendants. Just like those people that you saw protesting against the British decision to sell arms. These people truly care for Asaba. But Kate is like a fox, not as openly spiteful as a wolf but still cunning and secretive all the same. Onome, I hope you haven't told her any more about our discussion on Asaba. Everything that you tell her will be documented in her mind and for all we know she might have some connection to Asaba, which explains her preoccupation. Why else would she be reading an article about the Nigerian civil war and tell you about how it mentioned that Asaba was "calm", urging you not to be concerned? She didn't want you to believe me even though I was in Asaba whilst she was not. Does she think so little of me that I, as your best friend, would lie about something so agonising? Sorry to say this but I've never liked the girl from the moment you told me about her. I hope that now you truly understand why.*

I'm considering going back to Asaba to apologise to David and show him my appreciation for sending my letters to you. Can you believe that I refused to even say goodbye to Femi? He must be so distraught after everything that he has done for my sake! Right before I left, Femi and I were getting quite close, and I genuinely enjoyed spending time with him. Since I'm not happy here in Lagos I wouldn't mind going back to Asaba. At least there I have people who'll listen to my concerns and even if they don't, it won't hurt as much as knowing that my own parents aren't willing to.

Take care of yourself. I know that you have thousands of troubles to confront. But don't forget to take time to yourself. Occasionally, do something that you enjoy. I still remember how much you love to write. Maybe try writing and expressing your thoughts whenever you have some time. Never forget that I'm always thinking about you.

Folake

18th March 1969

Dear Diary,

The longer I stay in Lagos, the more I start to miss Asaba. There's not a day that I wake up to silence. The sound of cars, hustle for trade, and people's quarrels sound through my window. When I was staying at David's, even hearing the traffic of cars would be peculiar. Though many families own goats, chickens, cats and dogs, the sound is more soothing and organic to me. In Asaba the streets were calm and quiet, the morning breeze cool and comforting.

Today, my father came to my room. He apologised but still stood firm in his belief that talking about Asaba could get me in trouble. Though he refused to speak about Asaba, he did open up about his thoughts on the civil war more generally which brought a smile to my face. His opinion changes every day. Initially my father supported the Nigerian government because he believes that Nigeria is strong and assertive when unified. But after the massacre occurred, he became very ambivalent with regards to the war. He reminded me not to forget that though Bendel State is not part of Biafra, we are still Igbos and proudly so. It made me glad to know we share similar views on the matter.

Before we could speak more the phone started to ring from the kitchen. It had to be at the exact moment I was speaking to my father about the war! He ran out to get the phone, leaving the door open. I listened in. He seemed to be speaking with a friend about the war. I tried my best to listen to what he was saying but all I could make out were complaints of children dying, and his condemnation of the Biafran government for not surrendering or attempting to negotiate with the federal government to put an end to their misery. Then he started whining about a man called David Hunt. "That stupid David Hunt is a useless man. High commissioner for nothing." was what I heard him say.

Later that evening.

I couldn't stop thinking about my father's mention of David. The name had too much of a fresh presence in my mind and, as I thought, in Onome's most recent letter, I found it. His name was there. In black ink staring at me from the page. She described him as none other than Kate's father! I must write to Onome before it's too late. She needs to stay away from him and his daughter!

Reflecting on what my father said, I cannot prove much to Onome. I know that David Hunt is a very common name and there are perhaps hundreds of men called David Hunt in Britain so how can I just assume that it is Kate's father? But there's still something in my mind telling me that it's him. Didn't she mention how he was very educated about Nigeria and even recognised her name as one that comes from the Midwestern region? Also, she told me about a suspicious paper that she had found at Kate's place. Onome assumed that it was owned by Kate, but it would make more sense if it belonged to her father. After all, she is David's daughter and so she would be aware of what her father does for a living. He has probably warned her about giving away too much information about Nigeria to Onome.

As I'm unfolding the different pieces of information that Onome has told me it is beginning to seem more legitimate. Whilst I have never been particularly fond of Kate, perhaps she is not the enemy, and it is her father who is the real villain. Whilst Onome and I are trying to find a means of broadcasting the truth about the Asaba massacre, a new hunt has appeared, and the truth must be uncovered.

18. Onome

Dear Folake,

I hope you're alright. You sounded so disheartened in your last letter and I want you to know that everything's going to be fine. Don't speak like that! Even though you're currently facing so many horrific events, you must remain positive for me, yourself, and Chukwuemeka.

Now, I'm just glad that you believe that it's me. This paranoia that you are experiencing fostered by your suspicion of David is deeply saddening. Especially since he has done nothing wrong. If it wasn't for David, we wouldn't have been able to contact each other. I wouldn't have been aware of the atrocities committed in Asaba nor would we have been able to communicate with one another about everything unfolding right before our eyes. I truly believe that you should try and see him somehow, either that he comes over to Lagos to visit you or you go back to Asaba as you mentioned. I feel horrible for discouraging you from telling him about our plans. I'm equally to blame for your distrust in him and I'm very sorry for that. I just wanted to ensure that you were safe. It's not easy for me to fathom how you could safely live in a house with two men that you hardly even know. It's natural for you and me to have our fair share of doubts about their trustworthiness, especially after what you witnessed the federal soldiers doing to innocent civilians.

Oh, my sister, I'm so saddened by how your parents have been treating you. From what you're telling me I'm finding it difficult to recognise aunty Nnenna and uncle Okorie anymore. I'll never forget how vocal your father was during the period leading up to our declaration of independence. How he would attend every single protest and create propaganda posters every Sunday encouraging the Nigerian people to fight for their independence from British colonial rule. He doesn't seem like one to bow down to authority and lower his voice in fear of facing punishment. Censorship must really be at extreme levels in Lagos for it to cause your parents to behave in such a manner. This has only given me more incentive to broadcast the truth about Asaba. I truly cannot believe it! For your own sanity, it might be better for you to go back to Asaba. But that will take a lot of convincing to your parents. I doubt they'll allow you which is understandable because there is a civil war going on and they would fear losing their daughter. Travelling must be very stressful and dangerous. You never know who you could be stopped by. I'm even afraid of you going back to Asaba for your own safety. We've just started writing to each other again and if you travel to Asaba that will leave me in the dark about your whereabouts for such a long time. I remember the last time I didn't hear from you; it was a period of worry, concern, and fear for me. I don't wish to experience that again.

My friendship with Kate hasn't been the same since the dinner incident. We hardly see each other and the moments that we do are filled with awkward tension and silence. We no longer have deep conversations about history and politics, nor do we share our experiences at university. After the newspaper incident, I stopped telling her about the contents of our letters. I'm ever so thankful that I

134

did because I cannot even begin to imagine what she would've done with the information had I given it to her. It would be like feeding a dying lion in the zoo only for it to attack you afterward. My only worry is that I've confided in her about most of the events that happened prior to that. She knows about the massacre and that you saw it with your own eyes. She also sensed how eager I was to read the article which probably tells her that I lack trust in her words. Only God knows what she might be plotting against us. But I still don't understand why she would care. Perhaps you're right, she might just be an Africa fanatic. Quite a strange description for the Kate that I know of but at times you may not know anything about the people that you're closest to. Whilst she comes from a wealthy background and though I was initially concerned about our cultural differences, I believed that we could look past that. Perhaps I was wrong for being so naive.

I'm glad to hear that you like Ruth. She truly is an intelligent woman. Remember that I told you about a Daily Sketch newspaper that I took from the Daily Times office? I didn't see any information that was relevant to the massacre but

135

when I gave it to Ruth to read, she noticed something. In the article, it stated that "federal troops are making a triumphant advance in the Midwest", which means that they blatantly refused to highlight the massacre in Asaba by praising the federal troops' advance. She's a genius! Without her wisdom, I wouldn't have been able to grasp that the article was making any form of subtle reference to Asaba. This is further proof that the British press has taken the side of the Nigerian government. I even wanted to tell Ruth about Kate, but I need to find out the truth behind everything first.

Now I'm faced with another problem. Peter, my support officer, recently informed me of a missing Daily Sketch newspaper in the cabinet at the office. He was the one who gave me access to it, so he surely suspects that I was the person that took it. I denied taking it and told him that I don't recall seeing it so hopefully that is enough to steer away his suspicions. But I remain doubtful. Peter sounded very stern and subtly implied that there would be an investigation to find out who took it. All this nonsense just for a newspaper that is not even owned by them! The British never cease to amaze me with their misplacement of priorities. Whilst there are innocent civilians perishing in Nigeria, instead of sharing the news with their large audience they are running around in search of a newspaper. Their behaviour is very pathetic! Hopefully, this is all soon forgotten as they will not be receiving their newspaper back because I cut out the article referencing Asaba. That leaves a huge hole in the middle of a page which will make it very easy for Peter to point me out as the thief.

I fear that I'm in trouble. The sooner we do something about Asaba the better. I doubt you will have time to interview people anymore especially since you're all the way in Lagos and everyone is too afraid to speak about it. On my end, I have enough evidence to claim that the British press is undermining the extent of the Asaba massacre. Lest we also forget that our letters are an important source of evidence. If I get all of our letters together, we could use our conversations to expose everyone, from the Nigerian government to the Nigerian army to the British press. I'm not exactly certain how I'll go about publicising our letters. Maybe I could ask Ruth or there might be a way to make use of them at my internship. I wish Kate and I were still on good terms because then I could've asked her father whether he knows anything about publishing. He seems like such an inquisitive man full of knowledge about every aspect of life. If he knows the origins of my surname, then I wouldn't be surprised if he knows about the publishing industry.

You must do a huge favour for me. Could you send me all the letters that I've sent to you? We could use them to finally tell the world about the Asaba massacre. Our letters could provide a similar account of the Asaba massacre from your perspective and the rife censorship that has been adopted by the Nigerian and British governments from both our perspectives. From the tragic death of Chukwuemeka to the newspapers that I've found denying any form of gratuitous violence in Asaba. A farfetched objective but one that I'll commit to shaping into a reality for both of us.

Onome

3rd May 1969

Dear Diary,

Kate was the menace that I should've feared all along.

She came to see me earlier in the week, even though we had been avoiding each other for months. My biggest regret was letting her into my home. She didn't even have the decency to let me lead her into the kitchen. Instead, she walked straight past the kitchen and into my room. Sitting down on the bed like she owned the place.

The doorbell rang again just as I went to join her; a delivery man had arrived with some takeaway food. I assumed Kate had ordered it. For a moment, I was thankful. Until I returned to see my bedroom door pushed almost closed. When I looked through the crack, Kate wasn't on my bed anymore. She was crouched on the floor looking through my drawer of evidence. Oh, what a fool I was!

She looked up at my sound of outrage and I told her to leave immediately, throwing the takeaway bags into her arms as she scurried off.

What a pathetic diversion. Once she was gone, I checked my drawer only to find almost all my evidence missing. She had taken almost everything, leaving me only with the *Daily Times* article about Asaba. As betrayed as I felt, I was also scared. Scared that she knew what I was up to. She had the *Daily Sketch* article that I took from work. The one that could get me into huge trouble.

Kate did precisely what I feared that she would do. I barely had a chance to follow her before she so willingly told Peter everything, knowing how hard I worked to get this internship. She didn't even take the time to understand why I did what I did, nor did she ask. Peter simply couldn't trust me anymore. So, in the blink of an eye, he terminated my internship contract as my theft was a breach of regulation. All he could do was wish me luck with my studies and future career, now tarnished because of sly Kate. Kate has ensured that I will never be able to work at the *Daily Times* again.

I'm feeling very sorrowful and regretful. I regret putting so much effort into this plan only for the chances and opportunities offered to me at my internship to be left in ruins. Kate is a coward.

Regardless of her father and her own priorities, she shouldn't have done what she did. I needed to speak to someone about what had happened, I was so distraught. My first resort would usually have been to send a letter to Chioma but I couldn't wait. I had to talk to someone in person. Ruth was the only person that I could confide in.

Ruth and I met in the same café as usual, where I explained the whole situation, from exactly how I got the newspaper that she read to Kate's visit and the eventual loss of my internship. But what Ruth proceeded to say startled me. She told me that Kate wasn't to be feared even though it was due to her that I now no longer worked at the *Daily Times*, a dream workplace for thousands of students in London. She thinks that one of Kate's parents could be involved in Nigerian affairs and so they have inflicted their beliefs onto their daughter. She even thinks that the paper I saw in her house was one of Kate's parents' work materials. I can understand what she means by this because it would be so strange for it to belong to Kate. Kate could've been trying to protect her parents by preventing me from reading its contents. Her mother was so quiet and

141

seemed purely domestic, whilst Kate has mentioned that her father is politically engaged. Though she has never previously mentioned the exact role he has. Mister Hunt was so well-informed about Nigeria but seemed quite disinterested in me. Had he been interested in what I had to say about the civil war he would've stayed for dinner. Though Ruth made several valid suggestions, it all seemed very hyperbolic.

But there is one thing that Ruth told me that lightened up my face. She told me about the great importance of the letters between Chioma and me, and that evidence of the *Daily Sketch* letter exists within our letters. This is very true as I tell Chioma about all the information that I find that relates to Asaba in one way or another. After all, from reading our letters people can then locate the article in the *Daily Sketch* as it'll always be available to read, having already been published for the whole of Britain to read.

I was having similar thoughts last week, that is why I wrote to Chioma asking her to send all the letters that I've sent since the Asaba massacre with her next letter. I'm still not sure exactly what I can do with the letters but I'm just thankful that I came to the realisation of their evidentiary value. Whilst we are still in contact with one another, Chioma and I need to do all in our power to give Asaba a voice.

19. Chioma

8th June 1969

Dear Onome,

You're so right about the pressing need for us to publicise our letters. We may not be Anne Frank, but our letters discuss an undermined set of events that the world needs to know of. We have discussed violence, death, and grief. All of which relate to the Asaba massacre. I remember when we read the diary of Anne Frank in our penultimate year of secondary school. It was such a sad story but one that needed to be told. If she didn't write in her diary and if her diary was never found her story would have gone unnoticed and we would never know about her experiences. Gathering our correspondences will serve as a testament to Asaba and all that happened there. I'll send all your letters to you with this one that I'm writing. It'll be quite expensive, but my father knows how much I appreciate having the chance to write to you. Onome, if all goes wrong then promise me that you'll keep those letters in a safe place and that you'll never let them go?

It's going to be severely difficult not having your letters within my reach. Whenever I feel down, I always pick them up and read through everything that you have sent me. It's comforting reading your words knowing that you still exist in my life. But fear not, because I'm going to Asaba next week. I managed to get in contact with David to apologise. To make up for what happened, he has offered to organise a safe car ride to take me to Asaba. I leave for Asaba next week and I'm very excited to go back and see David, Femi and Aunty Amaka. I thought that David would never want to speak to me again, but he seems very understanding of my actions. Unfortunately, I'll be leaving Lagos without telling my parents. I already know that if I were to tell them they would do all in their power to prevent me from going. But I'll be leaving them a note before I leave. I feel that they deserve that from me especially after losing Chukwuemeka. If I were to just pack my bags and leave without informing them, only God knows what they could think would've happened to me. I

145

don't want them to live in a constant state of anxiety.

Whilst I'm on the topic of going back to see David, the name David has been circulating in my mind these past few days. Do you know of a man called David Hunt? Is he really Kate's father as you wrote to me a while ago? I recently overheard a telephone conversation between my father and someone else and he mentioned the name David Hunt in an irritating tone, calling him a "High Commissioner for nothing". It must be Kate's father! It all seems too convincing. Especially with Kate's swift dismissal of my experiences in Asaba by telling you about the Daily Times newspaper and the document concerning affairs in Africa that you found in her house. I truly believe that that document belongs to her father and her defensive response to your blatant interest in it was only to protect him. After all, we mustn't forget that he is her father.

Nevertheless, I don't think that Kate is the one to be most worried about. She's simply guilty by association but she's not the main perpetrator, David Hunt, her father, is. It's bizarre that when you told me about David Hunt you spoke of him as a man who is very knowledgeable about Nigeria. He even knows the origins of your surname! Is that not suspicious to you at all? What is an English man's concern with Nigerian surnames? He must have some connection to Nigeria to be so well-informed, which is probably his occupation. One doesn't just sit around reciting and learning the historical roots of names of people with entirely different cultures to oneself. We need to stop seeking validation from the white man and be proud of our heritage! His awareness of the roots of your last name shouldn't excite you, rather it should leave you concerned as to where he received such information from. Please stay wary of that man and if possible, avoid him at all costs. I would've told you to try and find out from Kate about her father's exact occupation, but I don't want to place you in any excess danger. It would be selfish of me. Also, though Kate might not be as dangerous as her father potentially is, she's still not to be trusted. If she was to come to you and willingly tell you about her father, then that would be immaculate. But I would discourage you from seeking that information yourself. It's too risky!

On that note, Onome, ensure that you keep all this evidence very safe so that your internship people do not find it! If they do you would certainly lose your internship which will be detrimental for you as an aspiring journalist and for our plan too.

I regret to say that you'll probably not be hearing from me for a while because I'm travelling back to Asaba soon. But I promise you that I'll send you a letter as soon as I get there. David has promised that he will continue to send my letters as he used to. He knows that I'm coming because I managed to call him the other day whilst my parents were both out. Take care Onome, this is not a farewell letter, it's one that will be continued. You'll hear from me as soon as possible. Never forget to take great care of our letters, they're our last hope in any darkened situation!

Folake

P.S.
Find attached all your wonderful letters.

20. Onome

20th July 1969

Dear Chioma,

You might not even receive this letter because you're not yet in Asaba. Rest assured that I've sent this letter to David's place and not your parents, so it'll be a wonderful welcome gift for you once you arrive. Thank you very much for sending all my letters to me. From now onwards any letter that I send to you will be written twice so that I can keep one for myself for my later plans. It must have cost a fortune to send all those letters to me, so you won't have to do it again. Whenever you do get the chance, thank your father for me. As I was flicking through all of our letters, I was astonished to see how much we have written. The content of our letters is so enriching yet troubling. If one were to read them in order, they would get a full scope of the rife censorship of the Asaba massacre. I tend to shudder with nervous excitement at the thought of it.

149

I'm very happy that you've decided to go back to Asaba. I think it'll make you much happier than if you stay with your parents in Lagos. Meanwhile, I'm also proud that you felt it necessary to write a note to your parents. As devastating as it must be for them, especially your mother, at least they're aware of your whereabouts. Especially after the situation with Chukwuemeka, it's so important for them to know whether you are safe or not. The car journey will be a long, tiring one but probably filled with suspense all the while. Try getting some quality sleep during the journey but make sure to also stay alert just in case you are stopped for some reason. I know that that is bound to happen during a civil war but I'm sure the driver that is coming to pick you up is well-versed in that field so try not to worry too much! As I'm writing this, I'm just realising that you cannot even take my advice because you won't even read it before travelling. How silly of me! But I don't mind because it feels therapeutic for me to do so.

Now back to the most surprising element of your letter. This David Hunt speculation is frightening me. Though I highly doubt that it's him, as David Hunt must be a very common name. It's fascinating to read how much your opinion of Kate has changed. Not so long ago you used to despise her and thought that she was the root of all evil. But now you suddenly believe that her father has been the evil spirit lurking around me. Even though I barely know the man and he barely knows me. I've known Kate for much longer and from what I've gathered he is a wealthy man who works a demanding job in England. I sincerely doubt that he has any business in Nigeria, please believe me. Kate, on the other hand, is all that you have claimed her to be. She managed to steal the latest article that I found and went as far as reporting me to Peter. I found out by phone call that I'd lost my internship. An offer that I've worked so incredibly hard for. I went through mountains and rivers to achieve what I so yearned for. Now it's been taken away from me, because of her.

I don't think Kate's spiteful behaviour came out of nowhere. I think that Kate envied me during our friendship. There was a turning point when I received acceptance to the internship at the Daily Times, whereas she was rejected. Kate pretended to

151

be happy for me but her disappointment couldn't be contained. It was a role that we both really wanted. During the waiting period, I had assured Kate that she would get the job because of her vast experience, fluency in multiple foreign languages, and astonishing grades. In the same breath, I sought to belittle my intelligence and suitability for the role as I was so certain that I wouldn't get it. She never told me any different, which affirms she thought I was inadequate. For me to get the role, she must have resented me deeply.

Chioma, have a safe trip to Asaba. Whilst you're on your way I hope that you reduce your tone and refrain from being vocal about Asaba. The last thing you want to do is get yourself in any unnecessary trouble. Hopefully, by the time you get to Asaba, I would've published our letters in some shape or form. Believe in me, I'll get it done. Trying to keep all my evidentiary material is difficult and is slowly becoming impossible because of the enemies that I have against me. It's saddening.

Onome

<u>Part 3.</u>

3 months later

21. Onome

5th October 1969

Dear Diary,

We're now in the dark days of October. Exactly two years ago, soldiers brutally assaulted the people of Asaba. A lot has happened over the past few months. The day after I sent my letter to Chioma, I decided to ask Ruth if she knew anyone by the name of David Hunt. Though I expected her to dismiss me, her reaction confirmed Chioma's intel. Ruth knew exactly who David Hunt was, telling me that he was the British High Commissioner to Nigeria and a very spiteful man. I was also shocked that he, an Englishman, held a high position and engaged in Nigerian affairs. It was then that I began to question whether Chioma was right, that it was Kate's father.

As expected, Ruth insisted that I don't completely discard the idea that David Hunt could indeed be Kate's father. She told me a lot of things that were consistent with Chioma's judgement. That

Kate might not be as spiteful as I thought she was. That maybe her father was the driving force behind her deep suspicion of the events in Asaba. That her father might've been the one who told her to search through my belongings in my room. It seemed absurd to me that a man of his age and rank would be interested in stagnating my plans for little Asaba.

Ruth invited me back to her flat to confirm David Hunt's identity, sifting through a filing cabinet to retrieve an academic journal. She opened it on a spread page; I didn't even need to flick through the article to find him. The name David Hunt was in bold letters at the top and underneath was a small image of him. He had thin lips, ears that stuck out, wrinkly skin, and his hair was gelled back to the side. His arrogant face leered up at me: Kate's father.

When I told Ruth, she was outraged. Not at David, or at Kate, but at me. She told me that she didn't appreciate how I was so protective over the information that I knew about Asaba and the civil war. Had I told her about Kate's father the day I met him, along with his peculiar knowledge about Nigeria and his name, she would've been able to inform me about his identity long ago. But I didn't even suspect anything so how could I possess the benefit of hindsight? She didn't even attempt to understand the situation from my naive perspective. Kate was my friend, so it was difficult for me to suspect such ulterior motives from her, let alone her own father. I couldn't stand and listen to her scream at me about something that I had no control over, so I left her flat in anger. She let me scatter like a wave of birds. This occurred some months ago and since then our friendship hasn't been the same. We see each other every now and again but we're no longer discussing Asaba. She firmly refuses to do so.

Along with Ruth, I've also lost the most important connection to Asaba, Chioma. I've not heard back from her for months now. I know that she did tell me that it would take her a while to get to Asaba, but she mentioned that it would only take a couple of weeks. Months later, I still await to read her words. Perhaps she got there and is having issues with either Femi or David, or she is taking some time to herself? I'm not going to bombard her with letters in case it is the latter. But, I do want to know that she's alright and has reached Asaba safely. That's all I ask for.

10th October 1969

Dear Diary,

I have well and truly begun my final year at King's College. Usually, I would've gone back to Nigeria over the summer as my cousins have done in previous years, but civil war has prohibited me from even considering the idea. My mother has yet again sent me an item. I am so appreciative of these regular items because it reminds me that though they're facing civil war, they still live, and I can feel their presence. This time it's a photograph of my mother, my father and me the summer before the civil war began. We were in Lagos sitting in my uncle's compound smiling. I'm in the middle with my parents on either side. My father is standing tall like a soldier and my mother is slightly slanted. We are all wearing brown traditional attire, our collective favourite colour. Though I'm saddened that I won't be able to see my parents, I'm thankful that I have some time to make good use of these letters.

Later.

My dear Chioma is missing! The phone just rang, and I stopped writing to answer it. It was Chioma's mother. They don't know where she is and asked me if I had any idea. After some internal deliberation, I did give her David's address. If Chioma is safely at David's place and her parents end up going there to find her she won't forgive me. It would be a huge breach of our trust. But I refuse to believe that Chioma is sitting in David's parlour and has not thought to inform me. Something is wrong with Chioma, and I must find out. The only way I could do that was by telling her parents where she had meant to go.

When I eventually told them the address, I could hear Chioma's father shouting in the background, I couldn't make out exactly what he was saying but vaguely heard him mentioning travelling to Asaba himself. He sounded angry but at least he was worried about his daughter. Right now, my only concern is that they find Chioma and it doesn't spiral into more anguish. I have done what I felt needed to be done and now it is down to her parents to take it from here. It's their sole responsibility as parents.

11th October 1969

Dear David,

I don't know if you know who I am. Chioma has probably told you about me. After all, she's told me about you. Chioma has told me that you were the person enabling her to send letters to me. I'm very thankful for that as it bridged the communication gap that was caused by the civil war. I shall never forget your efforts, thank you, sir!

A couple of months ago she told me that she was heading back to Asaba from Lagos to see you and that you had organised her travel. Months have now passed and I'm yet to hear from her. She told me that she would send me a letter as soon as she gets to your place. Could you just confirm whether she has reached you safely? I would love to know that my best friend is safe. You're the only person who can confirm this.

I've been meaning to send this letter to you for a while but some days ago I received a call from her parents asking me if I knew where she was. That was my breaking point. It gave me the courage to

161

request this information from you. Her parents knew that she was going to Asaba, but Chioma didn't tell them the address that she was going to. So, I did. Please, if they haven't visited you yet and Chioma is there, warn her for me of their upcoming arrival.

I regret involving you in this complex situation, but I couldn't listen to her mother's cries and not inform her of the place her daughter was heading to. It would've been cruel of me to do so. But I do apologise all the same. It must be frustrating having to deal with this when you're not at all involved. Nevertheless, my advice to you would be to prevent involving yourself when they do arrive. Let Chioma take care of the explosion that might occur. But don't let her walk into it blindly, inform her what I've told you. I would really appreciate it. Take care!

Onome

17th November 1969

Dear Diary,

Somebody special paid me a visit today. My hands are shaking just thinking about when I opened the door to see her. I must have cried out so loudly that they heard me in Paris! In front of me was my best friend, one that has been so far away from me for so long, Chioma. I haven't had a chance to properly speak to her yet, she's fast asleep on my sofa. She's badly hurt, bandages all over her head. She hasn't told me anything yet. She will when she wakes up. For now, I've left her to rest.

The excitement of seeing her almost stopped me from writing this diary entry. However, today was momentous in more ways than one. I went to the library to borrow a journal on Nigerian contemporary politics hoping to find some more information about David Hunt. I scanned the different paragraphs of varying lengths and I noticed that there was a section on the Commonwealth and underneath there was a description of David Hunt, the British High Commissioner to Nigeria. The more I read the more stunned I was to see that Kate's father is a man of significance.

The words that were being used to describe Mister Hunt were staggering and difficult to read. He was shown as a triumphant supporter of the federal government and their cause of reuniting Nigeria. He doesn't at all support or sympathise with the Biafrans, describing them as traitors and instigators. I keep thinking back to our conversation in the car. He didn't at all strike me as someone who held such radically inclined views. He must be aware of the Asaba massacre as British High Commissioner to my country. It's impossible for him not to know about the impunity committed by the federal soldiers inflicted on the people of Asaba. That alone infuriates me.

I presume he views Nigerians as puppets who simply succumb to the state and aren't worthy enough human beings to deserve rights. I might be a hypocrite condemning David for supporting a united Nigeria even though I held similar views before the massacre occurred. But his views don't stem from patriotism and a value for independence from colonial rule, he's supporting a united Nigeria for the sole purpose of self-interest. A united Nigeria is more economically advantageous for Britain. A divided Nigeria will only cause disruption to the post-colonialist, exploitative system that they have so perfectly built.

The letters are the only source of information that is of value to me. Though the newspapers that I've found are very useful, Kate and David Hunt know that I have access to them. But as for the letters, they remain completely ignorant of my possession of them. It's my only hope in these troubled times. Inside my black box underneath my bed bears history. Our letters span over two years, and they outline key developments in Chioma's life during and after the massacre as well as my efforts to fully understand what occurred. Some of the letters have tears in them whereas others have splatters of tea on them. Each set of letters smells different. Chioma's letters remind me of Nigeria, the smell is strong, and it hits you like a bus speeding on a road. It is filled with a mixture of scents from herbs to dust. The smell of dust increases and the herbs decrease after Chioma moves to Lagos, as the atmosphere in Lagos is more urbanised than rural Asaba. My letters on the other hand smell of cigarettes and dampness. I don't smoke myself, but I assume that the postman that collects the mail is a religious smoker. As for the dampness, it could be due to all the rain in London. Those letters could have easily been confronted with rain along their treacherous journey to Nigeria.

22. David

5th November 1969

Dear Onome,

I hope that this letter finds you well. Where do I even begin? Unfortunately, Chioma is not with me currently so I cannot pass your message to her. I've not heard from her either for a while but in this letter, I'll tell you all that I know. I believe this will help you on not only your but our mission to find her as paradoxically we in Asaba are in search of her whereabouts too.

To somewhat alleviate your pain, I can confirm that Chioma arrived in Asaba. She arrived a lot later than we had all anticipated that she would, and she arrived alone without my childhood friend Joseph. I didn't even need to question his absence because simply looking at the state of Chioma staggering at my doorstep sealed his fate for me. She was holding her chest area and there was blood all over her shirt. She was walking with a limp and her face looked harrowed like an old woman's. Femi and I were panicking but we didn't want to frighten her even more, so we brought her in. I gave her fluids and herbs whilst Femi went to Aunty Amaka's house as Chioma managed to tell us her address.

At that moment when it was just Chioma and I, I had so many questions for her, but I was unsure of how to articulate them. I was also weary of hammering her with questions when she was in such a critical condition. I simply consoled her and hoped that she would have the strength and will to inform me about what took place. She did. She told me that she and Joseph had gotten into a car accident on the way to Asaba. She told me that the Joseph that I'd known for almost my whole life was dead. He apparently died in a collision that happened on the road. Though Chioma was also badly injured she managed to survive. Chioma tried to get help, but nobody was willing to offer aid and at the sound that authorities were coming to attend to the situation Chioma knew she had to leave. After all, that was what Joseph had advised her to do, to stay far away from the authorities. By then she had barely reached Benin City and she began to run with no direction at all. Chioma herself didn't go into as much detail so I don't know exactly how she eventually made it to my place, but she did tell me that a young couple saw her running a few days after the accident and stopped their car. They asked where she was headed, and she took the risk of telling them as she knew that she had no other option. Lucky for her they were kind-hearted individuals with no ounce of ill intent within their bones so they accommodated her for a few days before setting off to Asaba. They knew that they couldn't afford to drive her to Asaba straight away because she was in a devastating condition and had not eaten in days. She later found out that they were fiancés, and the soon-to-be husband was a trained doctor. He examined Chioma when they got back and though he couldn't absolutely confirm his examinations, he did think that she had busted ribs and was at risk of developing brain complications due to the head impact she experienced as a result of the collision.

When Femi finally returned with Aunty Amaka that was when the wahala started. I could hear her screams and cries from down the street, so

169

I already knew that she was soon approaching. When she got in, she immediately examined her niece as expected. At that point, I was trying to get to grips with the reality that I had lost my good friend and that Chioma was so physically hurt. Aunty Amaka, a short and busty woman, took some documents out of her bag. It was an approved visa. She made some important phone calls and the next day Chioma left for Lagos again to get on a flight to London. Chioma was just as shocked as I was about how quickly Aunty Amaka managed to perform such productivity before our very own eyes. I cannot even imagine how afraid Chioma must have felt knowing that she was to set off to Lagos the next day in a car, the very type of vehicle that almost cost her her life. But I think she knew that the safest option was to take the opportunity that was presented before her.

The day after Chioma had left for Lagos her parents showed up at my place. Unfortunately, I didn't receive your letter before so it came as a shock to me. Regardless, I thank you for your compassion in thinking it was necessary to inform me as I was indeed not prepared for what was to occur. I tried to explain the situation to them, but their emotions were too overpowering for me to contain. Whilst Chioma's mother was praising God for her daughter's survival, her father was furious at hearing his daughter was being sent to Britain for treatment, his anger more geared towards Aunty Amaka than Chioma herself for leaving. I never really understood why he was so angry at Aunty Amaka for helping his daughter using all her existing funds. Femi, again, went to get Aunty Amaka. An explosive scene of events unfolded upon her arrival. They were speaking a lot of Igbo, possibly to ensure that Femi and I didn't understand. Femi is obviously Yoruba, so he was very unaware of the context of the entire conversation. I don't know whether they thought I was Edo or Urhobo because I don't have an Igbo first name and I grew up in Benin City but unfortunately for them, I understood every single word that they said.

Chioma's father was angry at Aunty Amaka for a lot of reasons. But the principal one seemed to be her decision to send Chioma to Britain for treatment. He called her a thief and told her to go to a dibia to assist her in "staying away from manly

171

roles". He told her that it was his role as a father to protect and financially provide for his child. From what I gathered, Aunty Amaka is a widow who was married to a very wealthy man, and she acquired some of his wealth upon his passing. As such, she's in a much better position financially than Chioma's father. Though she is his senior sister I can somewhat sympathise with his rage because it wasn't her place to use her own money for Chioma's trip to, and eventual treatment, in Britain. However, that didn't warrant such a response from her father who most likely didn't have enough money to do so. I remember Chioma told me that her parents were working in Lagos to gather funds for her visa application and studies abroad. Chioma's critical condition meant that she could've easily died had Aunty Amaka waited for his consent and funds which he didn't possess. Chioma's father seems to be a very traditional man who is blinded by his ignorance.

One valid accusation he did make however was that Aunty Amaka spitefully sent his daughter away with the approved visa that he worked so hard to get without acknowledging his efforts. He told her how he was against Chioma's tendency to speak about Asaba as he and his wife had plans to send her to Britain so that she could start a fresh life and leave the traumas of Nigeria behind her. He sent the visa confirmation to Aunty Amaka when he received it because he didn't know that Chioma would come to Lagos during the war. Both her parents had received it recently and wanted to surprise Chioma once they had made enough money collectively to support her tuition fees abroad. They thought that telling her about the approved visa and not yet having enough money to send her abroad would shatter her aspirations and give her false hope. From what I recall Aunty Amaka didn't mention her parents when informing Chioma about the visa and so I perceived it to have been due to her efforts alone. However, in her defence, the visa was soon expiring and Chioma's father insisted that he had almost raised enough money and was to send her to London within the next few weeks. Whether or not this is true certainly remains an entire mystery.

I'm not yet through with everything that Chioma's father accused Aunty Amaka of. There's more to come, unfortunately. He also mentioned

173

how it was largely her fault that Chioma had been living in my place after the massacre. He was constantly calling her for updates and her response was always very nonchalant. He claimed that she didn't look hard enough for her. Aunty Amaka herself who was initially supposed to have taken part in the welcome ceremony wasn't present because of her illness at the time. I think this has really pained him because though ill, she dodged a bullet not attending, whilst both of his children had to experience such a disastrous occurrence, which resulted in the death of one of his children. It would explain why Chioma was always so worried about Chukwuemeka as opposed to Aunty Amaka because she was probably certain that her aunt was safe and far away from all the suffering masses not only because of her absence but also due to her attained social class as the wife of a wealthy man. Additionally, he was also furious at how she had decided to send Chioma to a foreign country alone in such a devastating condition, claiming that she could die along the way and that if she was truly adamant about doing this, she should have followed her. Though I doubt Aunty Amaka had enough money to travel with her.

She responded to all these accusations with a similar tone to Chioma's father, contesting how he was ungrateful and envious of her financial successes. She called him a liar for claiming that he had enough funds to send her to Britain and told him that the visa would've expired if she had waited for him. I could see the pain in Aunty Amaka's eyes when she told him that she was only trying to do what was best for her niece and that he didn't know how hard she looked for both his children when the massacre happened, sending spies across the town and ordering relatives to locate their whereabouts. As I had rightfully assumed, she expressed that she couldn't afford to go to Britain herself and assured him that she'll do all she can to maintain contact with Chioma. Though now we've all lost contact with her. We know that she got to London and was admitted into St Mary's Hospital but haven't heard from her nor the hospital about her current condition. If you could somehow visit the hospital or give them a call, we would all really appreciate it. Thank you Onome! I know that this letter is

175

extremely lengthy, but I felt that you deserved to know the truth and only the truth. Take care and don't hesitate to write back to me if there is anything you need!

David

23. Onome

18th November 1969

Dear Diary,

Chioma awoke late the morning after she arrived. It was her, alive and in flesh. I gazed at her; she looked the same as she did when I last saw her before I left for Britain. She still had her hair in a low cut and beautiful almond eyes with brown skin. Her lips were still full, and her nostrils were large like mine to deal with the heat of the African sun. The only difference that I noticed was a large bandage wrapped around her head underneath her headwrap and that she looked facially exhausted.

Chioma told me that she got into a car accident on her way to Asaba and that David's best friend Joseph who was driving unfortunately passed away. By the look on Chioma's face, I could tell that this has severely affected her, and she tried to blame herself for his loss, but I assured her that she had nothing to worry about. Whilst inside I was still grappling with the fact that she was here, this man

177

Joseph was dead, and Chioma was very close to suffering a similar fate.

Aunty Amaka is the one who helped Chioma to travel to Britain. She gave her a visa which had been approved by authorities and funded her travel and the treatment that she received at the hospital. Chioma told me how everything happened so fast and that she's ever so grateful for her kindness and gratitude. It was comforting seeing her smile thinking about her great aunt. I'm shocked that Aunty Amaka would do such a thing. Not because she doesn't love and care for her niece but because it would have cost a fortune to fulfil. Not only that but also sorting out the visa must've been a long and draining process to go through. But nevertheless, I'm over the moon that my best friend has finally returned to me and that she's hopefully here to stay. I cannot even imagine how traumatising it must've been to experience a car accident and I cannot begin to fathom the amount of physical and emotional pain that Chioma would've experienced.

Whilst Chioma and I were gisting in the kitchen I got a response from David. When Chioma saw the letter from David she let out a nervous smile. We both sat in silence and read the words of the letter avoiding eye contact the entire way through. The more I read the less inclined I was to look over at Chioma who was shaking her head in disbelief. I got teary-eyed at the tone in which David wrote about the loss of Joseph and his worries surrounding Chioma's state. He really is a man of virtue, and we initially doubted his intentions. In life, it tends to be the kindest people that are portrayed as disingenuous in our eyes. He wrote in such a tender manner and expressed his emotions to the fullest despite not knowing me personally. I appreciate that.

24. Chioma

18ᵗʰ December 1969

Dear David,

Where do I even begin? Firstly, thank you for writing to Onome. I finally reached her recently and, little did I know that you had gone so far as to write to her to get in touch with me. This warms my heart. I'm ever so appreciative of your worries and concerns. Your kindness does not go unnoticed. Coincidently, we received your letter shortly after I arrived and both read through it. It was so heart-warming reading your deep concerns and hope despite losing Joseph, yet simultaneously it was equally heart-breaking reading about the awful behaviour of my family members. Their actions only confirm why I don't always agree with the saying that 'blood is thicker than water'.

Onome has offered to accommodate me for the coming weeks whilst I'm healing from the injury and has also promised that she'll guide me through my attempts to find somewhere else to live later. I

*feel bad staying with her and eating her food. It's a
similar kind of guilt that I felt when I was living with
you and Femi. Though I'm very appreciative of all
of you, at times it can get quite overwhelming
knowing that you're a burden on somebody else's
property. Before arriving at Onome's flat I stayed in
the hospital for several months. The staff were kind
but stern and I received different types of
medication that I cannot even name. The worst part
of my stay there was the nights, as that was when I
was left alone consumed in my thoughts. It was
horrible, I felt so lonely and homesick. I would just
stare into the ceiling and imagine how phenomenal
it would feel to be able to walk free of pain again.
To be healthy and vibrant and not worry that
touching my head would cause an aching pain or
that stepping too hard on the ground would cause
my knee to jolt in agony.*

*David, I know that I've asked you for many
favours, but please inform my family that I'm safe.
Though I'm not particularly happy with how they've
handled this situation, I still care deeply about them.
The last thing that I want to do is leave them
unaware of my survival. That would only cause a*

further spiral of anger and guilt within their dynamic. Exactly what I wish to avoid. Please send them my regards and let them know that I'm so appreciative of their efforts to get me to where I am today. Tell them that they shouldn't fight because of me and instead should be grateful for my flourishing. I have put them through so much stress with my indecisiveness and troubles concerning Asaba and despite this, I'm so very happy to be starting afresh now. That's all I will write with regard to my family, I don't wish to discuss family issues with you because you don't deserve to hear all of that. You're neither the cause nor the perpetrator of this nonsense.

Lastly, I would like to extend my thanks to both you and Femi. If Femi hadn't taken me from the crowd the day of the massacre and had you not been willing to take me into your home, only God knows where I would've ended up. I thank God every day for both of you. The world needs more caring and righteous people like the two of you. Had everyone been like you then we wouldn't have massacres and wars going on. Though I certainly wrongfully doubted your intentions initially and even poured out my anger onto you when I feared that you were betraying me, I want you to know that I'm so sorry for my despicable actions. I don't think I've ever told you how sorry I am, and you are deserving of that. For all you've ever been is kind to me. You took me in as a stranger and welcomed me with warm arms. Whilst my brother was in danger, I was safe, and I often took it for granted. This injury has taught me so many life lessons. That one should always thank the ones around them who are contributing to their life and never take anything for granted. You had every right to reject Femi's proposal to accommodate me had you wished because living with a stranger is so difficult. I was so busy feeling sorry for myself and worrying about Chukwuemeka that I failed to acknowledge the enormous lifestyle shift that my coming must have posed to your life. For that, I'm ever so sorry, David.

I don't know exactly what the future holds for me here in London but what I'm certain of is that I will never forget you or Femi. The two of you will always be dear to my heart. We should keep in touch through letters as Onome and I once did. Just send them to this address and I'll inform you if anything does change to my living situation. Greet Femi for me. Take care!

  Chioma

20ᵗʰ December 1969

Dear Diary,

Writing that letter to David was difficult. Despite being glad to finally be able to reconnect with him, at the same time it feels as though I'm saying farewell. As though I may never see him again even though I promised to keep in contact. If I don't even know when the next time I'm going to see my parents will be then that leaves me clueless as to when I'll ever be able to reconnect with David and Femi in person. I was so happy to see Onome. I can't believe every morning I wake up she'll be there.

Today, there was a knock at the door. Onome went to answer it and I remained seated. I could hear a woman's voice. I feared that it might've been Kate. If it were her, I would've shown her out myself. After everything she put Onome through! As I turned down the hallway, I saw an African woman with an afro and a brown headband standing by the door. She looked roughly thirty years old and was carrying a brown bookbag in her right hand. Once she saw me, she instantly smiled, showing all of her white, shining teeth. She introduced herself as Ruth. Ruth, the woman who Onome met at the protest and who told her about Asaba! We were both excited to meet each other. If it weren't for Ruth, Onome probably wouldn't have had the courage to take the neglected massacre in Asaba to greater lengths. It might've gone by as another mass killing in Africa. Just as if Onome hadn't told me about Ruth's distraught that day then I might not have felt it necessary to tell Onome about the welcome ceremony in such vivid detail. Just like David, Ruth was the connecting thread to our story.

Ruth joined us at the table, and we spoke about the massacre in Asaba for ages. Onome told us about how ironic it was that we both helped her find out who David Hunt was, the father of her once-good friend. It's astonishing how well-connected we all are in our thoughts despite barely knowing each other. It appears we were destined to find each other and tell the story of Asaba. This is all made possible through the spectacular work of our Almighty God! Ruth urged us to do something with the letters. She believes that they seem to be rotting away before our eyes yet they're so rich in value. She was right, those letters mean everything to us, and they couldn't just sit in Onome's room waiting to be stolen and destroyed by some thieves. So Onome went to go and get the letters, leaving Ruth and me alone in the kitchen. When we were alone Ruth told me how proud she was of my bravery and gave me a piece of paper. It had her number on it. If I'm ever in need of anything she expects a call from me. It is so nice knowing that so many people are willing to help me in such a desperate time.

Onome brought the black box of letters to show us. I looked at them, scanning through every single individual paper. There were over twenty pieces of paper stacked on top of each other. I felt a rush of nostalgia looking at them. Those letters included everything that had impacted Onome and me since we had made the decision to send letters to each other when the civil war began. I was initially confused as to why Onome was so persistent on me sending my letters from her to Britain but looking at them all neatly organised into one unit I began to

187

understand why she felt it was so important. The sad truth that we had to confront was that the series of letter-sending had come to an end and as we couldn't physically publicise them, it also ended our over-anticipated plans for Asaba.

Just when we thought all hope was lost, Ruth gave us a phenomenal idea. She told us that our letters in themselves were a fight for Asaba, that they gave a voice to the unheard. She advised us to store it in a sacred place that nobody knew of until we felt ready to use them. So, we allowed Ruth to pick this so-called 'sacred place'. After a long drive, Ruth parked her car by the Hyde Park entrance and told us to get out. The place was beautiful with green grass and flowers growing everywhere. The sun shone on the grass illuminating the green colour. Ruth told us she was taking us to a place where she liked to sit and reflect whenever she felt stressed. Some playful skips later and there it was. A tree with a large circle of dry mud surrounding it. Onome and I were confused but Ruth was in awe. Initially, I found it so difficult to see why Ruth would take us to such a specific tree. There were plenty of other sophisticated trees that she could've chosen. Like an oak tree that was just a few metres away. We were to bury the letters in the dirt. Ruth went to go and sit on the bench some metres away leaving Onome and me to carry out the burial.

This is where I got emotional. As soon as Ruth sat on the bench Onome and I stared at each other, teary-eyed, and began to silently weep. We knew it was soon over. This was it. Our letters and our search for Asaba had come to an end. I could already imagine our lives carrying on, so swiftly that we wouldn't even have time to think about Asaba. Onome would soon graduate. Meanwhile, I wanted to start university in the coming academic year. After that, we would probably get married and have children. Would we then still have the time for Asaba? Would we still be so dedicated to uncovering the truth and bringing it to light?

I looked down and saw Onome crouched down on her knees using a stick to dig into the dirt and form a hole to place the letters in. Seeing her in that state reminded me of the very first day that we met each other. The day that I saw her on her own using sticks to dig into the dust in our school compound. Though I was very young at the time, I

189

knew that we were destined to be best friends. There was a particular aura about her that made me gravitate toward her lonely game of digging that afternoon. Onome dug a hole big enough to fit the bunch of letters in. She sat and stared into it for ages.

Then, she dug into her black bag and brought out a paper and pen. She told me something so spectacular. That just in case we never get the chance to come back here to make use of the letters we needed to write one final letter. To the person who is going to find these letters and hopefully fulfil the dream that we couldn't do. I would've never thought to do such a thing. This is what I adore about Onome. She's constantly steps ahead.

Onome handed me the paper and pen and I walked over to the bench that Ruth was standing by and wrote:

20th December 1969

Dear whoever has found this treasure,

This is Onome and Chioma. We're so thankful that you've found our letters. If you have, this means that we were unable to do what we desired to do with them. Not because we are unambitious and dispassionate, but because we lacked the resources to do so. But hopefully, you do. Take these letters and read them. They account for a time in our lives in which I, Chioma, was experiencing the Asaba massacre of October 1967 during the Nigerian Civil War. Meanwhile, Onome was living and studying in Britain and saw for her own eyes the blatant censorship of the massacre.

May these letters not be misused. Use them to elevate not only our voices but the hundreds of unheard voices of those who were killed at the massacre. Share our words with the world, don't be afraid. If we were able to risk our lives as we did on several occasions in this series of letters, then you should be alright. If you, like us, don't feel equipped to do something tangible with these letters then don't worry. Simply hand them over to someone who can. But if you don't know of anyone who can, don't fret! We advise that you dig another hole in the same spot where you found these and bury them once again. These letters shall remain here until someone out there in the world is able to use them for good. Thank you!

Onome and Chioma

As soon as I finished writing it, I stumbled back to Onome and handed it to her. She read it and stared back at me with a look of joy, pride, and sorrow all at the same time. She unravelled the red ribbon, placed the letter at the front of the stack of papers and re-tied the letters together. This time without hesitation she tenderly placed the letters inside the hole and placed dirt on top till they were no longer visible. This was it. Onome kissed her hand and placed it on top of the buried letters. I did the same, whilst struggling to bend down. Onome got to her feet, and we held hands and walked towards Ruth who was smiling from the bench. When we got to Ruth, she took my right hand and we jointly walked back to the car in unison.

Though we might not have fulfilled our dream of publicising the events in Asaba, we hope that our collection of letters one day will be found and that the story of the Asaba massacre doesn't die in vain. However long it may take, just knowing that it will one day be found and spoken about leaves us all at peace. For Asaba will not fade into silence.

Acknowledgments

A Letter Away From Asaba is certainly not a book that was created individually. Many minds and words were influential in granting me the tools to write the story of Onome and Chioma.

I would like to give special thanks to my family for providing guidance and support during the process of writing and publishing my debut novel. A huge thanks to my mother who continuously listens and engages in my endless conversations about history, tribal conflict in Nigeria, and self-constructed theories about why the world is the way it is. Also, for her support for my spontaneous idea to expand my university experience by writing this novella. Great thanks to my father who also grew up with a passion for writing and would sit down with me as a child as we'd collectively write stories about princesses and fairies. I will never forget the endless copies of my short stories that I got you to print out for me at work practically every day.

To Lily, my editor, it has been a pleasure to work with you on my manuscript. Your support and editorial insight have helped me shape the book into a piece of work that I'm immensely proud of, that speaks to the reader so eloquently. Our compatible author-editor relationship made the editing process both enjoyable and seamless.

To Quinthia, my cover designer, working with you on the book cover has been wonderful. Your artistic abilities and eye for detail created a figurative image that is representative of the narrative. The day you

194

sent me the final version of the cover design remains firm in my mind defined by a burst of joy.

Professors Elizabeth Bird and Fraser Ottanelli's 'Asaba Massacre: Trauma, Memory and The Nigerian Civil War' is a notable mention. Reading this book back in 2020 enlightened me about the Asaba massacre and the censorship of the event which enabled me to create a fictional narrative centred around the Asaba massacre.

Great thanks to my good friends Deborah and Mendii who witnessed the ups and downs of the publication process and provided their support and guidance. Deborah, for your relentless support throughout the entire process constantly offering to read parts of my manuscript that I wanted readership insight on. Mendii, for your great advice on concerns that I had and inspiration on how to put myself and my book out there even when I was reluctant. I wish I could name the entire list of wonderful friends and associates who offered different kinds of support like reading parts of the manuscript, listening to my ideas, and understanding in times I couldn't join for coffee or a night out in first year. As I write this, I get flashbacks to fruitful conversations with Amanda and Hazel in various cafés in Edinburgh and inspirational chats with my good friend Paula at that Starbucks in London Victoria Station. To all my friends who have listened, supported, or helped in any way (you all know who you are), I thank you all so much! Your love and support does not go unnoticed.

A Letter Away From Asaba was written to commemorate the victims of the Asaba Massacre in hopes that the historical tragedy becomes more identifiable and accessible to public consciousness. Through reading this historical fictional narrative, I hope it inspires people to seek out their history and immerse themselves into crucial historical discourse.

CLAUDIA EFEMINI

Claudia Efemini is a current History and Politics student at the University of Edinburgh (2021-2025). Born and raised in London, Claudia spent the latter part of her upbringing in Sweden before moving to Edinburgh to pursue her undergraduate degree in 2021. An aspiring journalist, Claudia is a frequent writer of articles pertaining to a variety of topics from history and politics to philanthropy. Claudia wrote her debut novel 'A Letter Away From Asaba' during her first year of university.

38060400R00116